Sexually Transmitted Diseases

ISSUES

Volume 10

Editor

Craig Donnellan

Independence

Educational Publishers

Cambridge

First published by Independence
PO Box 295
Cambridge CB1 3XP
England

British Library Cataloguing in Publication Data
Sexually Transmitted Diseases – (Issues Series)
I. Donnellan, Craig II. Series
616.9'51

ISBN 1 86168 189 5

Printed in Great Britain
The Burlington Press
Cambridge

Typeset by
Claire Boyd

Cover
The illustration on the front cover is by
Pumpkin House.

CONTENTS

Chapter One: Sexual Health

Chapter Two: HIV and AIDS

Introduction

Sexually Transmitted Diseases is the tenth volume in the Issues series. The aim of this series is to offer up-to-date information about important issues in our world.

Sexually Transmitted Diseases examines the issue of sexual health including HIV and AIDS.

The information comes from a wide variety of sources and includes:
Government reports and statistics
Newspaper reports and features
Magazine articles and surveys
Literature from lobby groups
and charitable organisations.

It is hoped that, as you read about the many aspects of the issues explored in this book, you will critically evaluate the information presented. It is important that you decide whether you are being presented with facts or opinions. Does the writer give a biased or an unbiased report? If an opinion is being expressed, do you agree with the writer?

Sexually Transmitted Diseases offers a useful starting-point for those who need convenient access to information about the many issues involved. However, it is only a starting-point. At the back of the book is a list of organisations which you may want to contact for further information.

*****

Sexual health in England today – setting the scene

Information from the Department of Health

Introduction

Our sexual health affects our physical and psychological wellbeing and is central to some of the most important and lasting relationships in our lives. It follows that protecting, supporting and restoring sexual health is important.

The Government's strategy for sexual health and HIV proposes a comprehensive and holistic model.

Sexual health is an important part of physical and mental health. It is a key part of our identity as human beings together with the fundamental human rights to privacy, a family life and living free from discrimination. Essential elements of good sexual health are equitable relationships and sexual fulfilment with access to information and services to avoid the risk of unintended pregnancy, illness or disease.

The problems

Rising infection rates, the arrival of the HIV epidemic in the 1980s, evidence of increased risk taking and – often – poor control of infections, have all helped to raise the level of concern among health professionals, the Government and the public. The most common conditions now are Chlamydia, non-specific urethritis and wart virus infections, but almost all sexually transmitted infections (STIs) are becoming more common.

The number of visits to Departments of genito-urinary medicine (GUM) in England has doubled over the last decade[1] and now stands at over a million a year. Diagnoses of genital Chlamydia also almost doubled during the 1990s, with a particularly marked increased in men and women aged under 20. Recent surveys of women indicate Chlamydia[2]

- Sexual health is an important part of physical and mental health.
- Sexual health problems in England have grown in recent years.
- More HIV infections are being diagnosed and sexually transmitted infections are rising.
- England has the highest teenage birth rates in Western Europe.

infection rates of up to 12% and there are more reports of outbreaks of syphilis.[3] The number of HIV infections newly diagnosed in 2000 was the highest since reporting began.

Many sexual infections have long-term effects on health. Some genital wart infections are associated with cervical cancer, as is Chlamydia.[4] Left untreated, Chlamydia can result in pelvic inflammatory disease which can lead to ectopic pregnancy and infertility.[5]

Consequences of poor sexual health

- Pelvic inflammatory disease, which can cause ectopic pregnancies and infertility
- HIV
- Cervical and other genital cancers
- Hepatitis, chronic liver disease and liver cancer
- Recurrent genital herpes
- Bacterial vaginosis and premature delivery
- Unintended pregnancies and abortions
- Psychological consequences of sexual coercion and abuse

Sexual health is a key part of our identity as human beings

- Poor educational, social and economic opportunities for teenage mothers

International comparisons

England is not unique – other European countries have similar problems. France, the Netherlands, Sweden and Switzerland have all reported increases in gonorrhoea between 1995 and 1999,[6] particularly among men having sex with men. The same group has also suffered outbreaks of syphilis.

Despite the rise in newly diagnosed infections, HIV prevalence in England has stayed low compared with some other Western European countries. This reflects prompt action on a number of fronts: health promotion, needle exchange schemes and other harm minimisation initiatives, screening of blood and clinical interventions, the availability of open-access GUM clinics and careful surveillance and analysis of trends.

HIV

An estimated 30,000 people are living with HIV in the United Kingdom, of whom a third are undiagnosed. There is still no cure. There probably won't be a highly effective vaccine for at least five years. About 400 people a year die as a result of their HIV infection. The year 2000 saw the largest annual number of newly diagnosed HIV infections since the start of the epidemic, and for the second year running the number of new infections acquired through heterosexual sex outnumbered those acquired through homosexual sex. However, three-quarters of these heterosexual infections were probably acquired abroad, which means that sex between men remains the major transmission route for HIV in this country. HIV prevalence by the end of 2003 is expected to be 40% higher than the 1999 level.[7]

Combination therapy has improved the lifespan of people living with HIV. Better survival rates combined with the growing numbers of new infections, mean that the number of people living with HIV is rising. Recently, there have been increasing concerns abut resistant HIV strains and their sexual trans-mission. All of these present some real challenges for long-term clinical treatment, care and social support, as well as for prevention of further transmission.

HIV therapies are complex, expensive and extremely demanding on the patient. The human costs for people living with HIV are high. Many cannot work, and others can still suffer ill-informed prejudice and discrimination. Children with HIV have an especially difficult time – as well as the effects on their own health they may face losing one or both of their parents prematurely.

Sexual behaviour & knowledge
Studies suggest there has been an increase in risky sexual behaviour, and that there is still ignorance about the possible consequences. The average age at which people start having sex is now 17. Forty years ago it was 21 for women and 20 for men. Between a third and a half of teenagers do not use contraception at first intercourse.[8] Over a quarter of 14-15-year-olds think that the contraceptive pill protects against infection.[9] In 1999 most people questioned in a national study did not know what Chlamydia was.[10]

Britain's African communities have been particularly badly affected by HIV/AIDS, with high rates among both adults and children

---

A 1999 survey of gay men showed that 58% of those under 20 did not always use a condom.[11] A recent study indicated that 44% of HIV positive men had anal sex with a new partner in the last month, of whom 40% reported no or in-consistent condom use.[12]

Inequality
Sexual ill health is not equally distributed among the population. The highest burden is borne by women, gay men, teenagers, young adults and black and minority ethnic groups.[13, 14] The rates of gonorrhoea in some inner-city black and minority ethnic groups are ten or eleven times higher than in whites.[15] HIV infection also has an unequal impact on some ethnic and other minority groups. Britain's African com-munities have been particularly badly affected by HIV/AIDS, with high rates among both adults and children.[16]

There is a strong link between social deprivation and STIs, abor-tions and teenage conceptions. Unintended pregnancies increase the risk of poor social, economic and health prospects for both mother and child. Girls from the poorest backgrounds are ten times more likely to become teenage mothers than girls from wealthier backgrounds.

References

1   *Trends in sexually transmitted infections in the United Kingdom, 1990 – 1999. New episodes seen at genito-urinary medicine clinics*: PHLS (England, Wales & Northern Ireland), DHSS & PS (Northern Ireland) and the Scottish ISD(D)5 Collaborative Group (ISD, SCIEH and MSSVD): December 2000, ISBN 09001144 49 5

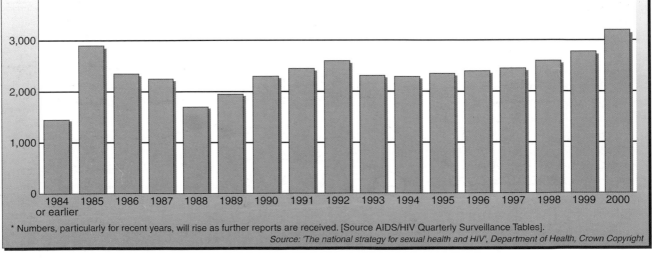

Newly reported HIV infections

Numbers* of newly reported HIV infections in England by year of diagnosis (data to end March 2001). The number of HIV infections newly diagnosed in 2000 was the highest since reporting began. Despite the rise in new infections, HIV prevalence in England has stayed low compared with some other Western European countries.

* Numbers, particularly for recent years, will rise as further reports are received. [Source AIDS/HIV Quarterly Surveillance Tables].
Source: 'The national strategy for sexual health and HIV', Department of Health, Crown Copyright

2 Stokes T, Screening for Chlamydia in general practice: Literature review and summary of the evidence; *Journal of Public Health Medicine* 1997 19(2), 227-232

3 CDSC 'Increased transmission of syphilis in Brighton and Greater Manchester among men who have sex with men': *Communicable Disease Report Weekly* 27 October 2000: Vol. 10 (43) 383-6

4 Anttila T et al. Serotypes of Chlamydia trachomatis and risk of development of cervical squamous cell carcinoma. JAMA 2001; 285: 47-51

5 Stamm W, Guinan M, Johnson C et al. Effect of treatment regimens for Nesseria gonorrhoea on simultaneous infection with Chlamydia trachomatis. *N Engl. J Mod.* 1984;310:545-9

6 Nicoll A, Hamers F F: Emerging trends in HIV, gonorrhoea and syphilis in Western Europe (in press/personal communication)

7 AIDS and HIV Infection in the United Kingdom: monthly report. *CDR* 2000, 10 (50), 453-4

8 Wellings K, Field J, Johnson AM, Wadsworth J. *Sexual Behaviour in Britain, The National Study of Sexual Attitudes and Lifestyles*, Penguin 1994

9 Health Education Authority, *Young People and Health*, HEA 1999

10 Dawe F, Meltzer M. *Contraception and Sexual Health 1999*: A report on using the ONS Omnibus survey produced on behalf of the Department of Health, National Statistics ISBN 1 88774 4136

11 Sigma Research. *Vital Statistics Findings from the National Gay Men's Sex Survey 1999*, July 2000 ISBN 0872956521

12 Imrie J, Davis MD, Black S, Hart GJ, Davidson OR, Williams IG, Stephenson JM. 'Meeting the sexual health needs of HIV-seropositive gay men in a pre-requisite to developing the next generation of prevention strategies'. (Oral presentation) 14th Meeting of the International Society for Sexually Transmitted Diseases Research (ISSTDR) and International Congress of Sexually Transmitted Infections, Berlin Germany. 24-27 June 2001

13 Lacey CJN, Merrick DW, Bersley et al. Analysis of the socio-demography of gonorrhoea in Leeds, 1989-93: *BMJ* June 4 1997; 314; 1718-9

14 Hughes G, Catchpole M, Rogers PA et al. Comparison of risk factors for sexually transmitted infections: results from a study of attenders at three genito-urinary medicine clinics in England: *Sex. Trans. Inf.* 2000; 76: 262-267

15 Low N, Daker-White G, Barlow D, Pozniak AL. Gonorrhoea in Inner London: results of a cross sectional study: *BMJ* 1997 June 14; 314 (7096): 1719-23

16 *Communicable Disease Report*, AIDS & HIV infection in the UK: monthly report; 26 April 2001: Vol. 11, No.17

• The above information is an extract from the publication *The National strategy of sexual health and HIV*, produced by the Department of Health.

Government to spend £4m on safe sex campaign

By Claire Cozens

The government is to spend £4m on the biggest safe-sex campaign since the late 1980s after new figures showed a huge rise in the number of cases of HIV, the virus that causes Aids, and other sexually transmitted diseases.

Plans for a two-year TV and newspaper advertising blitz are being drawn up by the department of health.

The campaign is aimed at combating the growing complacency among British adults, which is contributing to rising rates of sexually transmitted diseases.

Figures released by the public health laboratory service today showed that rates of gonorrhoea in England and Wales were now at their highest for a decade, while HIV infection has also reached record levels.

A record 3,425 cases of HIV were reported in the UK last year – a 14% increase on 1999 and the highest figure recorded in any year since testing became widely available 16 years ago.

Campaigners are particularly concerned about the rising numbers of young men and women contracting such diseases in recent years. Of the 6,223 new cases of gonorrhoea among women, 40% were in the 16-19 age group.

Department officials have been holding focus groups to draw up a brief for the campaign and will begin approaching advertising agencies later this year.

It will be the first major government campaign to address the issue since the hard-hitting adverts used to warn people of the dangers of Aids in the late 1980s.

The advertising campaign will focus on younger people in a bid to reverse the trend.

They will be warned that unprotected sex can cause infertility and other serious long-term health problems as well as the risk of contracting HIV.

Sexually transmitted infections

Information from the Family Planning Association (fpa)

Sex is a normal and pleasurable part of life, however, it is possible that if one person has an infection it can pass to another person through the close physical contact that happens when you have sex. Infections that are spread in this way are known as sexually transmitted infections (STIs). In 1999 over 590,000 people in the United Kingdom were diagnosed in GUM clinics with having a sexually transmitted infection.

The possibility of getting an infection may not be something that you have ever thought about. Finding out about STIs is one way of avoiding them. If you feel you need more information then don't be afraid to ask.

STIs are most commonly passed on through vaginal, oral and anal sex. You don't need to have a lot of sexual partners to get an STI although the more partners that you have, the greater your chance is that one of them may pass an infection to you. Common symptoms of an STI are:

- unusual discharge or liquid from vagina or penis
- pain or burning when you pass urine
- itches, rashes, lumps or blisters around the genitals or anus
- pain and bleeding during sex
- bleeding after sex and/or between periods.

Symptoms, however, can vary from infection to infection and many STIs show no symptoms at all. It is not uncommon to have more than one infection at the same time.

Most STIs can be completely cured if found early enough and may only require you to take a course of antibiotics.

However, if left untreated these infections can be painful and uncomfortable or at worst cause permanent damage to your health and fertility.

fpa
putting sexual health on the agenda

How to avoid sexually transmitted infections

Using a condom (male or female) correctly and consistently when you have sex will prevent the transmission of most STIs including HIV. However, there are also several things that you can do to make sex safer.

Be prepared

- Discuss with your partner before you have sex how you will both protect yourselves.
- Become familiar with how to use condoms.
- Have a supply of condoms ready (these are free from family planning and sexual health clinics).
- There are lots of choices of condoms so try a different one if you are not happy with the ones you use now.
- Learn about how infections are spread, what symptoms to look for, and where to go for help if you are worried.

Take action

- Have a routine check-up at a sexual health clinic (free!)
- If you or your partner have symptoms or think you might have an infection seek advice before you have any more sex.

- Tell your partner if you have an infection so they can be treated too.

Where to go for help and advice

Sexual health clinics specialise in diagnosing and treating all STIs. Most large hospitals have a sexual health clinic. You can find details of your nearest clinic by:

- calling fpa's helpline on 0845 310 1334 (Monday-Friday 9.00am-7.00pm).
- looking in the phone book under genitourinary medicine, STD or VD.
- calling the National AIDS helpline on 0800 567 123 (24hrs).
- calling NHS Direct on 0845 46 47 (24hrs).

Facts about sexual health clinics

- You can refer yourself to any clinic in the country.
- All tests and treatment are free.
- The service is completely confidential.
- Your GP is not informed without your permission.
- People of any age or sexual orientation can attend the clinic.
- If you have an infection then the staff at the clinic can give you help in working out how to tell your current and past partners.
- You may need an appointment so ring before you go.
- They can get very busy so be prepared to wait for an appointment and for the first visit to the clinic to take a couple of hours.

If there isn't a sexual health clinic near you then you can also get advice from your GP, your practice nurse or school nurse, a family planning clinic or young people's clinic.

- The above information is an extract from the fpa's web site which can be found at www.fpa.org.uk

Sexually transmitted infections

Data on STIs in the United Kingdom (1995 to 2000*)

Key points

- The rising trend in diagnoses of many acute STIs since 1995 continued unabated in 2000. As with previous years, the large and increasing numbers of diagnoses among teenage females and men who have sex with men are of particular concern.
- Between 1999 and 2000, diagnoses of uncomplicated gonorrhoea rose by 29% (10868 to 13967) in males and 24% (5006 to 6223) in females, reaching a ten-year high. Within England, the largest regional increase occurred in the South East Region (which excludes London) where diagnoses rose by 55% (803 to 1249) in males and 46% (326 to 477) in females.
- Diagnoses of genital chlamydial infection have risen sharply since 1993. Between 1999 and 2000, diagnoses rose by 19% (22596 to 26877) in males and 17% (30625 to 35688) in females. It is thought that in addition to any increased transmission, this rise is likely to be a result of increased testing due to heightened public and professional awareness of the infection.
- During 2000, almost 40% (2349 of 6223) of diagnoses of gonorrhoea and 34% (12055 of 35688) of chlamydial infections in females were in those aged 16-19.
- Between 1999 and 2000, diagnoses of primary and secondary syphilis rose considerably in males (153 to 248) and females (55 to 73). The majority of cases (249 of 326) were diagnosed in London, the North West and South East regions. In addition, 25% (18 of 73) of cases in females were diagnosed in the Eastern region, largely attributable to an outbreak in Cambridgeshire.[1]
- Diagnoses of gonorrhoea and chlamydia in men who have sex with men increased by 45% (1855 to 2693) and 36% (628 to 851) respectively between 1999 and 2000 – a considerably larger increase than that seen in either males in general or in females. Additionally, the increase in diagnoses of infectious syphilis

> *As with previous years, the large and increasing numbers of diagnoses among teenage females and men who have sex with men are of particular concern*

was partly due to a large increase (52 to 117) in cases in men who have sex with men, associated with outbreaks in Manchester,[2] Brighton[3] and London.[4]

- The sustained rise in diagnoses of STIs over the last 6 years is probably attributable to the increasing practice of unsafe sexual behaviour, particularly in young heterosexuals and homo/ bisexual men. In view of the severe longer-term complications associated with untreated STIs, as well as their potential role in facilitating HIV transmission, these latest data emphasise the need to improve current STI prevention strategies.

Selected conditions by sex

England and Wales, 1995-2000*

Syphilis (Primary and secondary)	1995	1996	1997	1998	1999	2000
Total males	103	86	100	87	156	253
(of which homosexually acquired)	36	20	19	23	52	117
Total females	31	34	50	44	55	73
Total	134	120	150	131	211	326

Gonorrhoea (uncomplicated)	1995	1996	1997	1998	1999	2000
Total males	6,764	8,067	8,599	8,569	10,868	13,967
(of which homosexually acquired)	1,372	1,710	1,804	1,697	1,855	2,693
Total females	3,395	4,073	4,071	4,172	5,006	6,223
Total	10,159	12,140	12,670	12,741	15,874	20,190

Chlamydia (uncomplicated)	1995	1996	1997	1998	1999	2000
Total males	13,304	14,528	16,789	19,622	22,596	26,877
(of which homosexually acquired)	237	282	356	463	628	851
Total females	17,122	19,165	23,410	26,088	30,625	35,688
Total	30,426	33,693	40,199	45,710	53,221	62,565

Herpes (first attack)	1995	1996	1997	1998	1999	2000
Total males	6,094	5,960	5,814	6,224	6,205	6,327
(of which homosexually acquired)	338	393	336	302	345	329
Total females	9,447	9,773	9,817	9,874	10,099	10,257
Total	15,541	15,733	15,631	16,098	16,304	16,584

Warts (first attack)	1995	1996	1997	1998	1999	2000
Total males	27,771	28,592	31,889	32,397	33,681	33,841
(of which homosexually acquired)	1,363	1,300	1,489	1,528	1,608	1,617
Total females	26,454	29,022	30,097	30,472	30,970	30,529
Total	54,225	57,614	61,986	62,869	64,651	64,370

* English and Welsh data for 2000 are provisional, as data for 2000 from Scotland and Northern Ireland are currently unavailable they been temporarily excluded from this table.

Source: Public Health Laboratory Service (PHLS)

References
1 CDSC Outbreak of heterosexually acquired syphilis in Cambridgeshire Commun Dis Rep *CDR Weekly* 2000;10:(45)
2 CDSC Syphilis continues to spread in Greater Manchester Commun Dis Rep *CDR Weekly* 2001;11:(15)
3 CDSC Increased transmission of syphilis in men who have sex with men report from Brighton and Hove Commun Dis Rep *CDR Wkly* 2000;10:(20)
4 CDSC Syphilis transmission among homosexual and bisexual men in London and Manchester Commun Dis Rep *CDR Wkly* 2001;11:(5)

* data for 2000 are provisional and currently unavailable for Scotland and Northern Ireland
• Diagnoses of selected sexually transmitted infections (STIs) seen in genitourinary medicine clinics: England and Wales, 1995 – 2000 (provisional data for 2000)

© *Public Health Laboratory Service*

Types of infections

Information from the Family Planning Association (fpa)

There are at least 25 different sexually transmitted infections. Below is some information about four of the most common: chlamydia, gonorrhoea, genital warts and genital herpes.

Chlamydia

What is it?
Chlamydia trachomatis is the most common bacterial sexually transmitted infection. The bacteria are easily transmitted and generally infect the genitals of men and women. It can also infect the throat and rectum (back passage). Using a condom correctly and consistently for vaginal, anal and oral sex provides good protection against chlamydia. The infection can also be passed from a pregnant woman to her baby during birth.

What are the symptoms?
It is estimated that about 50% of infected men and 70% of infected women have no symptoms at all. If symptoms are present they can show up at any time, from one week after being exposed to the infection to many months later.
• Women may notice an unusual vaginal discharge, pain when passing urine, and/or bleeding between periods or after sex.
• Men may notice a white/cloudy and watery discharge from the tip of the penis and pain when passing urine.
• Infection in the rectum rarely has symptoms but may cause discomfort and discharge.
• Infection in the throat doesn't have symptoms.

putting sexual health on the agenda

What tests are there for chlamydia?
There are several different tests that are effective at identifying the infection. In women these can involve taking a swab from the cervix (entrance of the womb) and the urethra (tube where the urine comes out) or testing a sample of urine. In men either the urine is tested or a swab is taken from the inside of the tip of the penis (urethral swab). Taking the swabs is not painful but can occasionally feel a bit uncomfortable.

What is the treatment?
Early treatment of the infection is simple and effective. The infection is usually treated with either a single dose of antibiotics or a longer course lasting up to 2 weeks. If complications have occurred other treatment may be required. It is important that all the antibiotics are taken and that there is no unprotected sex until the infection has gone. Once chlamydia has been successfully treated, it doesn't come back unless you get a new infection. However, there can be long-term problems following an untreated infection.

> *Once chlamydia has been successfully treated, it doesn't come back unless you get a new infection*

What happens if chlamydia isn't treated?
Without proper treatment the infection in women can spread to other reproductive organs and cause pelvic inflammatory disease (PID). This can, in turn, lead to long-term pelvic pain, blocked fallopian tubes, infertility and ectopic pregnancy (pregnancy that occurs outside of the womb). Chlamydia may also be linked with early miscarriage. In men it can lead to a painful infection in the testicles and possible reduced fertility. Sometimes a form of arthritis known as Reiter's syndrome occurs. This is more common in men.

Gonorrhoea

What is it?
Gonorrhoea is a bacterial infection that is sometimes known as the 'clap'. It is easily transmitted through vaginal, anal and oral sex. It commonly infects the genitals of men and women, the anus and rectum (back passage) and the throat. Using a condom correctly and consistently for vaginal, anal and oral sex provides good protection against gonorrhoea. The infection can also be passed from a pregnant woman to her baby during birth.

What are the symptoms?
It is estimated that about 10% of infected men and up to 50% of

infected women have no symptoms at all. If symptoms are present, they may show up any time between 1 and 14 days after being exposed to the infection.

- Women may notice an unusual vaginal discharge, which may be thin/watery or yellow/green and have a strong smell. There may also be pain when passing urine.
- Men frequently notice a white, yellow or green discharge from the tip of the penis and pain when urinating.
- Infection in the rectum is often symptomless but may cause a discharge from the anus, irritation or pain and bleeding.
- Gonorrhoea in the throat rarely causes symptoms.

What tests are there for gonorrhoea?
Gonorrhoea is looked for under the microscope and also grown in the laboratory. To do this, swabs are taken from the cervix (entrance of the womb), the urethra (tube where the urine comes out) and sometimes the throat and the rectum. Taking the swabs is not painful but can occasionally feel a bit uncomfortable.

What is the treatment?
Early treatment is simple and effective. The infection is usually treated with a single dose of antibiotics taken by mouth. If complications have occurred, other treatment may be required. It is important not to have unprotected sex until the infection has gone. A second test is often done later to make sure the infection has gone. Once gonorrhoea has been successfully treated, it doesn't come back unless you get a new infection. However, there can be long-term problems following an untreated infection.

What happens if gonorrhoea isn't treated?
Without proper treatment it can cause long-term complications. The infection in women can spread to other reproductive organs and cause pelvic inflammatory disease (PID). This can, in turn, lead to long-term pelvic pain, blocked fallopian tubes, infertility and ectopic pregnancy (pregnancy that occurs outside of the womb). In men it can lead to pain and inflammation of the testicles and the prostate gland.

Genital warts
What are they?
Genital warts are caused by a virus called Human Papilloma Virus (HPV). This is the commonest sexually transmitted infection seen at sexual health (GUM) clinics. Genital warts are small fleshy growths that may appear anywhere on a man or a woman's genital area. Warts that appear around the anus are known as perianal warts. Genital warts are spread through skin-to-skin contact and can be passed on during vaginal and anal sex. It is possible, although rare, to develop them in or around the mouth after oral sex with someone who has genital warts. It is thought to be rare that warts are transferred from the hands to the genitals.

What are the symptoms?
It is thought that only about 1% of people who become infected with the virus have any visible genital warts. When warts are visible they can take on a variety of appearances. They may be small white lumps or larger, cauliflower-shaped lumps. There may just be one or there may be many. They don't usually cause discomfort but may irritate and cause some inflammation of the skin. The development of visible warts is thought to take at least several months and possibly longer. If they do appear, they can be around the vulva, the penis, the scrotum or the anus. Warts can appear around the anus without anal sex having taken place. Warts are not always easy to see as they can develop inside the vagina or anus and on the cervix.

What tests are there for genital warts?
Diagnosing genital warts is usually done just by looking. There is no routine test that is done when visible warts are not present. If genital warts are suspected but are not obvious, a weak vinegar-like solution may be applied to the outside of the genital area. This turns any warts white. Diagnosis, however, is not always easy. To check for any hidden warts an internal examination of the vagina, cervix or anus can be carried out.

What is the treatment?
As genital warts are caused by a virus, antibiotics will not get rid of them. Unlike warts that appear on other parts of the body, there is no treatment of genital warts that can be bought in the pharmacy. The treatment that is given will depend on where the warts are situated, how many there are, their appearance and what is acceptable to the individual. There are several treatments. Two of the most common are painting the warts with a solution and freezing them. Sometimes more than one treatment is required to successfully get rid of warts. For some people, treatment can continue over a long period of time. It is not uncommon for warts to come back again in the few months after treatment. However, the longer warts stay away the less likely they are to come back.

Are there any long-term problems associated with genital warts?
Some women worry that, if they have had warts, they will go on to get cancer of the cervix. The types of HPV that cause visible warts are rarely associated with genital cancers. Not everyone decides to have warts treated and sometimes they go away by themselves.

Will using a condom protect me?
There is little research evidence to suggest that using condoms protects against getting genital warts although they will, of course, protect against other infections such as chlamydia, gonorrhoea and HIV. Using condoms while warts are being treated may help to make them go away more quickly. Some health

professionals believe that condoms help to prevent the spread of the infection if they are used for the first three months after treatment (as this is when warts are most likely to come back) and also when there are visible warts that can be covered by the condom.

Genital herpes

What is it?

Genital herpes is a common virus infection caused by the herpes simplex virus (HSV). There are two types of HSV that can cause genital herpes, type I and type II. Both of these can cause sores around the mouth (cold sores) and around the genital and anal region. The virus is spread by direct skin to skin contact. This can happen during vaginal, anal and oral sex and through kissing. It may also be possible to pass it on to a baby during pregnancy and birth.

What are the symptoms?

The majority of people who contract the herpes simplex virus are unaware that they have it. This could be because the symptoms are so mild that they are not recognised or because no symptoms develop at all. If symptoms do develop this may be as early as 4-5 days after contact with the virus but it could also be several weeks, months or possibly even years. This makes it difficult to know where the virus came from. The first episode of herpes often tends to be the most severe because the body has not had time to build up any defences against the virus. The sorts of symptoms that might be noticed are:

- A flu-like illness, backache, headache, swollen glands in the groin or fever.
- Tingling, itching, burning and pain.
- Small fluid-filled blisters which burst leaving sores which are sometimes painful.
- Pain when passing urine if this passes over the sores.

For a large number of people the initial outbreak may be all they experience. Those that do have further outbreaks find these are milder, become less frequent and the symptoms clear up more quickly. Further outbreaks may occur more frequently if HSV type II is present.

What tests are there for genital herpes?

Taking a swab from the herpes infected area and sending it to the laboratory to detect the virus is currently the most useful and common way of diagnosing the infection. From these swabs it is possible to tell what herpes virus type is present.

What is the treatment?

At the present time nothing is available to get rid of the virus from the body completely. When herpes is first experienced there are treatments (usually in tablet form) which if taken early can make the symptoms less severe and help to clear up the outbreak quicker. These treatments appear to have little or no influence on whether or not herpes returns. There are many things that people can do that help to reduce the symptoms of recurrent outbreaks, which may also prevent further episodes altogether. These include avoiding getting overtired or very stressed, eating a well-balanced diet, cutting down on smoking and excessive alcohol and avoiding direct sunlight on the site of the infection. In some cases the doctor may also advise taking tablets continuously.

Are there complications associated with genital herpes?

Genital herpes is not associated with cancer of the cervix and does not affect a woman's ability to become pregnant. Serious problems are uncommon. Women with genital herpes can experience a safe pregnancy and normal childbirth. If the first outbreak of herpes occurs in the first three months of pregnancy there is a small risk of miscarriage. If it occurs later in the pregnancy then specialist care may be needed but it is rare for any serious problems to occur.

Will using condoms protect me?

The effectiveness of condoms at preventing transmission of the virus has not been extensively assessed although there is some evidence that they may help. Avoiding contact with the infected area of skin during an outbreak and when the early warning signs of an outbreak are noticed may also help in preventing transmission. It is not clear how easy it is to pass the virus on when symptoms are not present.

More information about herpes can be obtained from the Herpes Association on 020 7609 9061.

If you would like information about other sexually transmitted infections you can telephone the fpa helpline on 0845 310 1334 or visit www.shastd.org.uk

• The above information is an extract from the fpa's web site which can be found at www.fpa.org.uk

© fpa

Sexual health for women

Information from Health Promotion England

Are sexually transmitted infections common?

Anyone can get a sexually transmitted infection if they have unprotected sex with someone who is infected. Sexually transmitted infections happen frequently in both men and women.

Some of the more common sexually transmitted infections include:

- genital warts;
- chlamydia;
- genital herpes; and
- gonorrhoea (the clap)

Often there are no symptoms, so you or your sexual partner could have an infection and not know it. Get medical advice straight away if you think you or your partner might have an infection.

Most sexually transmitted infections can be treated quickly and easily if you detect them early on. Some can cause serious long-term problems if you don't get them treated. For example, chlamydia and gonorrhoea can lead to infertility. And HIV infection is still a very serious condition, despite advances in treatment for many of the illnesses that people with HIV are likely to get.

You can reduce your risk of getting a sexually transmitted infection by doing the following.

- Always use a condom when you have vaginal, or anal sex and consider using one for oral sex.
- You can explore other ways of having sex such as kissing, stroking and touching.
- Use a dental dam (a thin latex-square barrier) to cover the vulva or anus during oral sex. You can get dental dams from some sexual health clinics, chemists and mail-order agencies. Contact the National AIDS Helpline for details free on 0800 567 123.

Most sexually transmitted infections can be treated quickly and easily if you detect them early on

---

- Put condoms on sex toys such as vibrators or dildos if they are being shared. Wash the sex toy between activities and put on a new condom for each partner and activity. Do not use the same condom for vaginal sex after you have used it in the anal area as you could transfer bacteria which may cause an infection in the vagina.

- You can use latex gloves with a lubricant before you insert a finger or hand in the vagina or anus.

Remember that symptoms may not appear for months, and some people get no symptoms at all. Others have symptoms which come and go even though the infection is still there.

Where can I get help?

Where to go for help

If you have had sex without using a condom with someone who has an infection, you could get an infection, even if your partner has no symptoms. Don't wait for symptoms to appear.

If you think you've been at risk, ask your GP for a check-up or contact an NHS sexual health clinic, often called an STD (sexually transmitted disease), or GUM (genito-urinary medicine) clinic.

NHS sexual health (GUM) clinics offer free checks and treatment for sexually transmitted infections. Some offer women-only sessions. The service is strictly confidential.

You can go to any NHS sexual health (GUM) clinic, anywhere in the country. You don't have to use a local one and you don't have to be sent by your GP. (Sexual health clinics which are not run by the NHS

do not always offer the full range of services you can get at NHS sexual health clinics.) You will not be tested for HIV without your consent.

If you don't seek treatment, the infection could get worse.

It's a good idea to have a check-up at an NHS sexual health (GUM) clinic if you have a new partner, or if either of you have more than one sexual partner.

What risks am I taking?

To make sex safer for you, you need to think carefully about the risks you face and take sensible steps to reduce them. These risks may change as your relationships and your lifestyle change.

Think about situations when the risks could be greater. For example:

- on holiday, take condoms with you – you never know when you might need them; and
- watch out for alcohol and drugs – they can change the way you behave and can affect the decisions you make about what is safe. You could end up doing something you regret later.

Be realistic – and plan ahead.

Condom talk

Many of us find it difficult to suggest using a condom with our partner. But once you have decided to have sex, the earlier you discuss it, the less likely you are to get carried away and end up not using any protection.

Try to get round to talking about safer sex. You can then let your partner know what you think and see how they feel too. You could be pleasantly surprised. Your partner may find it just as difficult to talk about it and would welcome your lead.

Many women carry their own condoms. If you are prepared it doesn't mean you are planning to sleep around – it is a responsible thing to do and shows you take your sexual health seriously.

- The above information is from Health Promotion England. Visit their web site at www.hpe.org.uk
© *Reproduced with permission from Health Promotion England. Crown Copyright*

Sexual health for men

Sexually transmitted infections

Check them out

Anyone can get a sexually transmitted infection if they have unprotected sex with someone who is infected. These infections happen frequently in men and women. You can have uncomfortable and painful symptoms. They disrupt your sex life and your partner's.

If you are sexually active, protect yourself and your partner by using a condom. You may risk getting and passing on sexual infections if you don't.

Warning signs you can look out for

- Discharge from your penis.
- Pain or a burning feeling when you urinate.
- Feeling that you need to urinate more often than usual.
- Sore testicles, itching, rashes, lumps, blisters or pain in your genital area.

Often you can't see the infection. You and your partner could have an infection without knowing it.

If you think you've been at risk, or you have symptoms of an infection, please get yourself checked out by a doctor or nurse.

Don't wait for the symptoms to clear up. Some symptoms do go away without you having treatment, but this doesn't mean your infection has gone away.

If your infection isn't treated, serious damage can happen. If you get help early on, most infections can be treated simply.

If you see anything or think you've been at risk, please get checked out straight away. You won't be wasting anybody's time.

Where can I get help?

- You can go to your doctor or an NHS sexual health clinic, sexually transmitted disease (STD) or genito-urinary medicine (GUM) clinic. These clinics give you free checks and treatment for sexual infections. Their service is strictly confidential, and nobody will know about your visit without your say-so.
- You can go to any NHS sexual health clinic without seeing your doctor first. If it is urgent, you don't usually need an appointment. But, please phone first.
- You can find information about your nearest NHS sexual health clinic by phoning the National AIDS Helpline free on 0800 567 123, or phone your local hospital and ask for the GUM clinic. Clinics will be listed in the phone book under genito-urinary medicine (GUM), sexually transmitted diseases (STD) or the old term, venereal diseases (VD). You can find information about clinics on our website: www.lovelife.uk.com
- NHS sexual health (GUM) clinics offer free HIV testing, and screening for other infections.
- Any information you give at the clinic is confidential.

- The above information is from Health Promotion England. Visit their web site at www.hpe.org.uk

© *Reproduced with permission from Health Promotion England. Crown Copyright*

Fertility bug shock

One in 10 young women has the life-threatening 'silent' disease

Shocking new figures reveal that nearly one in 10 young women has a sexual infection which can ruin their fertility.

A survey shows the highest recorded levels of chlamydia in sexually active women aged 16 to 25 – and most of the victims have no idea they have been infected.

Chlamydia, which is passed on through sex, is dubbed the 'silent disease' because it rarely produces symptoms.

But it can trigger pelvic inflammatory infection which may make women infertile or more likely to have a life-threatening ectopic pregnancy. Men are also victims of the disease but the lack of symptoms means they usually fail to get it treated and pass it on to sexual partners.

When chlamydia is diagnosed it can be treated with antibiotics.

Figures released today by the Public Health Laboratory Service show nine per cent of sexually active women under 25 have chlamydia infection.

The level is one-third higher than previous estimates and tallies with rises in a range of sexually transmitted diseases.

New cases of chlamydia for England and Wales increased from 53,221 in 1999 to 62,565 last year, an 18 per cent rise.

Gonorrhoea in England and Wales is also at its highest level for over a decade – increasing by 27 per cent last year alone – while syphilis is re-emerging with a 55 per cent rise in cases last year.

The latest figures come from a year-long pilot study of screening young women in two health authorities – Portsmouth and the Wirral – with the aim of establishing a nationwide routine testing programme.

A urine test was offered to women aged between 16 and 25 years attending their GP surgery,

*By Jenny Hope,
Medical Correspondent*

family planning clinic or hospital clinic for sexually transmitted diseases.

Dr Jeanne Pimenta, the study coordinator who will be presenting the findings today at the PHLS annual scientific conference in Warwick, said the results showed the potential benefits of nationwide screening.

Figures released by the Public Health Laboratory Service show nine per cent of sexually active women under 25 have chlamydia infection

The Government has already announced a TV and newspaper advertising campaign next year warning of the dangers of sexually transmitted infections, Aids and unwanted pregnancies.

There is concern about an epidemic of promiscuity and that

young people are ignoring safer sex messages advising use of barrier contraception such as condoms to prevent infection.

Experts believe their chief concern is avoiding pregnancy, not disease.

Dr Mike Catchpole, head of the PHLS chlamydia programme, said the study results showed young women wanted to have chlamydia testing and that GPs were keen to offer it.

Dr Catchpole said the new urine test enabled screening to be carried out at more convenient times for women, he added. Previously it had to be done at the same time as a cervical smear test.

The new test was also more accurate, giving at least 90 per cent accuracy rates, he said. This might explain why the study showed the highest ever rates of the disease because more infections had been missed using less accurate tests.

Dr Catchpole said it was vital to test women for the infection because untreated it could remain active in the body for around 14 months, during which time it can cause pelvic inflammatory disease and irrevocably damage the reproductive system.

This can lead to an ectopic pregnancy – where the fertilised egg lodges outside the womb – which is the leading cause of death during the first three months of pregnancy.

Under the Government's sexual health strategy, women attending family planning clinics and cervical smear appointments will be offered screening for chlamydia.

But Dr Catchpole said cervical smear appointments were given only to women aged 20 and over – which missed out on teenage girls. 'It is important GPs are involved so they can offer tests to girls aged 16 to 19,' he added.

© *The Daily Mail*
September, 2001

Where to go for help

Sexually transmitted infections

Where do I go for help?

If you think that you might have a sexually transmitted infection you should go to an NHS sexual health (GUM) clinic. These clinics offer free check-ups and treatment for sexually transmitted infections. They also do HIV testing. All information is kept strictly confidential. You can go to any clinic, anywhere in the country. You don't have to use a local one and you don't have to be referred by your GP.

You can find details of your nearest NHS sexual health clinic in the phone book under genito-urinary medicine (GUM), sexually transmitted disease (STD) or venereal disease (VD). Or you could ring the National AIDS Helpline free on 0800 567 123 for details of local clinics, or phone your local hospital and ask for the 'special' or GUM clinic. (Non-NHS sexual health clinics do not always offer the full range of services which are available at NHS sexual health clinics.)

Some sexual health clinics offer men-only and women-only sessions and some offer sessions for gay and bisexual men and women.

What happens at the clinic?

When you arrive, the receptionist will ask you to complete a registration form. You may then be given a card with a personal identification number to retain your anonymity.

You will be seen by a nurse, health adviser or doctor, who will ask you some questions about your general and sexual health. These include questions about your sexual activities and whether they were with a man, a woman or both. You may find these questions embarrassing but it is important that you answer them honestly to help staff find out which tests you need.

What tests are available?

- Once you have discussed your worries, the doctor decides what type of examination and tests you need.

A full sexual health check includes:
- An examination of your genitals and sometimes the lower part of your body, your mouth and skin.
- Taking a few swabs. A swab is a type of cotton bud used to pick up samples of any discharge or secretions from your genital region.
- A urine sample.
- A blood test for syphilis (offered to all patients).

You may also be offered:

- An HIV test. This will only be done if you specifically agree to it.
- A cervical smear test (if you are a woman).
- Blood tests for hepatitis B or C.

You may get some of your test results straight away. But other results take longer, and you must phone or call in to collect them. If your results show that you have an infection, you will be given treatment immediately.

If you are given antibiotics to take away, it is important that you finish the course – even if the symptoms go away before the tablets are finished. Do not share your treatment with partners or friends.

The clinic may advise you to contact any recent partners and ask them to attend for a check-up.

Can I still have sex?

It is better not to have penetrative sex until you have been given the all-clear. If you want to have sex while you or your partner has a sexually transmitted infection, ask your doctor or the clinic for advice. For some infections, for example genital warts, you may be advised to use a condom. If either of you have cold sores, don't kiss each other, particularly around the genital area, as this can pass on the infection.

An infection, such as herpes, which cannot be cured and is infectious during and possibly between outbreaks, doesn't mean the end of your sex life. Get advice from your doctor or clinic about how to make sex safer for you and your partner.

What if I am pregnant?

If a woman has a sexually transmitted infection during pregnancy, this could infect her baby either in the womb or during birth. However, most sexually transmitted infections can be treated during pregnancy without harming the mother or baby. Some infections, such as genital warts, can become worse during pregnancy.

During ante-natal care, tests for sexually transmitted infections are sometimes done to avoid possible ill-effects during pregnancy. These are not routine practice, but in some clinics where HIV is more common in the local population, HIV testing may be offered to all pregnant women.

Sexually transmitted infections during pregnancy can cause, among other things, miscarriage, abnormalities, eye infections, and lumps in the throat or genitals of the baby. It is also possible to pass on infections such as HIV and hepatitis B to the baby.

What do I say to my partner?

When you have a sexually transmitted infection, it is important to tell your sexual partner so that they can have a sexual health check-up too. If your partner also has the infection and does not get treated, you could get reinfected. Your partner will need to have a check-up even if they have no symptoms.

It may not be easy to tell your partner. Try to choose a good time to raise the subject – when both of you are relaxed and not likely to be interrupted. Try to share the responsibility. It is better to use phrases such as 'what are *we* going to do about this?' than 'what are *you* going to do?' Be aware that you or your partner may have become infected many months ago from a previous sexual partner without realising it.

Sometimes it is helpful if partners go to a clinic together. You will be

seen separately, but you can support one another and share advice and information about your sexual health.

'Partner notification'

If you think it is going to be too difficult to talk to your partner for any reason, you can send them a 'contact slip' which the clinic will give you. The doctor, health adviser or nurse can do this for you if you give them your partner's details.

The contact slip explains that the partner may have been exposed to a sexually transmitted infection. It suggests that they make an appointment for a check-up with their GP or sexual health clinic. Your identity and infection are not disclosed.

The contact slip is one way of notifying your partner. There are other ways. The doctor, health adviser or nurse will talk through the options with you. Nothing will be done without your consent. The clinic may not encourage notifying your partner if this is likely to place you in any danger.

Further advice

You can get free, confidential treatment and advice at any NHS sexual health (GUM) clinic or from your GP. You can find details of your nearest sexual health clinic in the phone book under genito-urinary medicine (GUM), sexually trans-

mitted diseases (STD) or venereal disease (VD) clinic. Or phone your local hospital and ask for the 'special' or GUM clinic.

You can find information about clinics on our sexual health website: www.lovelife.uk.com

If you have an urgent problem, most clinics will see you without an appointment. But it is better to phone first.

Clinic staff are there to help you, not to judge you. And remember, all the information you give them is strictly confidential.

Don't forget to keep any follow-up appointments to make sure that the infection has cleared.

If you have a sexually transmitted infection and are concerned about the possible effect the infection may have on pregnancy, ask the doctor, nurse or your midwife to explain this to you.

Remember, many sexually transmitted infections have no obvious symptoms. You can have an infection and not know it.

Remember that any information you give at the clinic is confidential.

• The above information is an extract from the leaflet *Sexually transmitted infections – How to prevent them, and where to go for help*, produced by Health Promotion England.
© *Reproduced with permission from Health Promotion England. Crown Copyright*

Aids – a global crisis

Westerners have become complacent about the dangers of Aids, say campaigners on World Aids Day

The world is in the grip of a global Aids crisis which affects 43m people – but in the West people have become complacent to the dangers. This is the message being pushed today, on World Aids Day, and campaigners have some chilling evidence for those who think the disease has nothing to do with them. Mark Oliver explains the threat.

How many people have Aids?
The Aids epidemic has so far left 50m people infected with HIV worldwide, of whom 16m have died. That leaves 34m people who are living with the infection. Africa has been the worst hit – 5,500 people die from Aids-related illnesses there every day. There are new fears that Asia may eclipse Africa in severity of infection levels. However, the steepest rise in infections in the world during 1998 was in the former Soviet Union and eastern Europe. There are 1.4m children with Aids worldwide.

But Britain does not have such a bad problem, does it?
As many as 10,000 people in the UK have HIV but are unaware of their condition according to a report published by the Department of Health. At the beginning of this year there were 20,800 people living with HIV – 40% up from four years ago. And the number of people diagnosed as HIV positive in England and Wales is set to rise by another 40% in the next three years. The public health laboratory service has warned that there will be 29,000 people who know they are HIV positive by the end of 2003. Last year saw record numbers of HIV diagnoses, with more than 3,000 new cases identified in England and Wales. Of around 30,000 people who are expected to

By Mark Oliver

be infected, about 16,000 will have been through homosexual sex, 11,500 through heterosexual sex and about 1,500 through drug abuse. It is estimated that a third of gay and bisexual men who are HIV positive do not know they have the infection

Last year saw record numbers of HIV diagnoses, with more than 3,000 new cases identified in England and Wales

and more than half of heterosexual men in London who are infected are unaware.

Are people being ignorant?
Campaigners say people who are too young to remember the massive Aids campaigns of the 80s are becoming complacent about the risks of the disease. A Mori poll of more than 2,000 people in the UK for the National Aids Trust found that despite multi-million-pound awareness campaigns, many people are still ignorant about the risks of becoming infected with HIV. One in 10 people wrongly believe there is a cure for Aids and a further one in 10 are not sure. Only a third of people aged 15-24 say that knowledge of HIV has made them change their lifestyle in some way – an 11% drop on the year before. A spokesman for

the National Aids Trust said: 'The fight against Aids is now a fight against complacency.'

Is there a cure yet?
No. The new and effective drugs have been responsible for fewer people developing full-blown Aids and increasing the numbers of HIV positive cases. But there is no cure.

What are the government doing to attack the problem?
The health minister, Yvette Cooper, has announced an extra £41m for health authorities in England to treat and care for people with Aids. Last year the government announced that all pregnant women would be offered an HIV test after research on HIV-positive pregnant

women in London found that 60% did not know they were infected before they conceived. Campaign posters, leaflets and an innovative website are being used in a 'make a difference' campaign by the National Aids Trust to encourage people to join the fight against the disease.

Facts about HIV/AIDS

Information from the United Nations Population Fund (UNFPA)

HIV/AIDS by Region

Sub-Saharan Africa
Sub-Saharan Africa is the hardest-hit region of the epidemic, although for the first time there are signs that HIV incidence may have fallen. In 2000, 3.8 million new infections were estimated, compared to a total of 4.0 million in 1999.

With just 10 per cent of the world's population, the region accounts for 71 per cent of people living with HIV/AIDS. The disease claimed an estimated 2.4 million lives in the region in 2000.

The total number of Africans living with HIV or AIDS is now 25.3 million. In 7 countries in southern Africa, at least one adult in 5 is living with the virus.

In 8 African countries, at least 15 per cent of adults are infected. In these countries, AIDS will claim the lives of around a third of today's 15-year-olds.

Asia
Compared to rates of HIV infection in Africa, those generally found in Asia are still low. Prevalence among 15-49-year-olds exceeds 1 per cent in only three countries – Cambodia, Myanmar and Thailand.

Still, the absolute numbers of HIV-infected people in Asia are large: some 5.8 million in South and South-East Asia (3.7 million in India alone), and about 640,000 in East Asia and the Pacific.

In South and South-East Asia, an estimated 700,00 adults, 450,000 of them men, became infected with

HIV in 2000, and 470,000 people died.

The disease is less common in East Asia and the Pacific, with some 130,000 new infections in 200,000, and 25,000 deaths.

Latin America and the Caribbean
Outside of sub-Saharan Africa, the Caribbean is the region hardest-hit by HIV/AIDS. Although rates of infection vary widely among the island states, an estimated 60,000 people were infected in 2000 in the Caribbean.

In Latin America, an estimated

150,000 people were infected with HIV/AIDS in 2000 and 50,000 people died from the disease.

An estimated 1.4 million people in Latin America, and 390,000 in the Caribbean are living with HIV/AIDS.

• For more information, visit www.unaids.org

• The above information is from the UNFPA's web site which can be found at www.unfpa.org

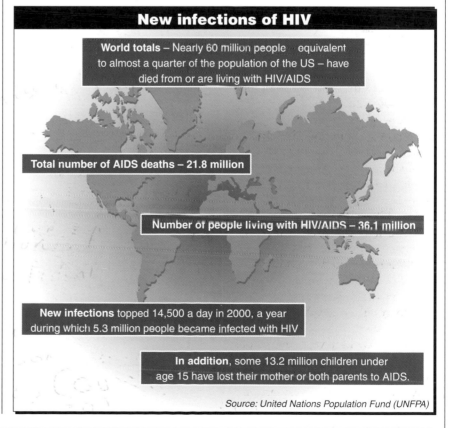

New infections of HIV

World totals – Nearly 60 million people equivalent to almost a quarter of the population of the US – have died from or are living with HIV/AIDS

Total number of AIDS deaths – 21.8 million

Number of people living with HIV/AIDS – 36.1 million

New infections topped 14,500 a day in 2000, a year during which 5.3 million people became infected with HIV

In addition, some 13.2 million children under age 15 have lost their mother or both parents to AIDS.

Source: United Nations Population Fund (UNFPA)

Worldwide HIV & AIDS epidemic statistics

Information from AVERT

People living with HIV

According to estimates from the Joint United Nations Programme on HIV/AIDS (UNAIDS) and the World Health Organisation (WHO), 36.1 million adults and 1.4 million children were living with HIV at the end of 2000. This is more than 50% higher than the figures projected by WHO in 1991 on the basis of the data then available.

Number of people infected during 2000, and the number of deaths

During 2000, some 5.3 million people became infected with the human immunodeficiency virus (HIV), which causes AIDS. The year also saw 3 million deaths from HIV/AIDS – a higher global total than in any year since the beginning of the epidemic, despite antiretroviral therapy which staved off AIDS and AIDS deaths in the richer countries.

Deaths among those already infected will continue to increase for some years even if prevention programmes manage to cut the number of new infections to zero. However, with the HIV-positive population still expanding the annual number of AIDS deaths can be expected to increase for many years.

Young people and children with HIV/AIDS and the AIDS orphans

Around half of all people who acquire HIV become infected before they turn 25 and typically die of the life-threatening illnesses called 'AIDS' before their 35th birthday. This age factor makes AIDS uniquely threatening to children. By the end of 1999, the epidemic had left behind a cumulative total of 13.2 million AIDS orphans, defined as those having lost their mother or both parents before reaching the age of 15.

In 2000, an estimated 600,000 children aged 14 or younger became infected with HIV. Over 90% were babies born to HIV-positive women, who acquired the virus at birth or through their mother's breast milk. Of these, almost nine-tenths were in sub-Saharan Africa. Africa's lead in mother-to-child transmission of HIV was firmer than ever despite new evidence that HIV ultimately impairs women's fertility: once infected, a woman can be expected to bear 20% fewer children than she otherwise would.

Men and AIDS

In all parts of the world except sub-Saharan Africa, there are more men infected with HIV and dying of AIDS than women. Altogether, an estimated 2.5 million men aged 15-49 became infected during 2000, bringing the number of adult males living with HIV or AIDS by the end of the year to 18.2 million. Men and AIDS will again be the theme for World AIDS in 2001.

HIV/AIDS around the world

The overwhelming majority of people with HIV, some 95% of the global total, live in the developing world. That proportion is set to grow even further as infection rates continue to rise in countries where poverty, poor health systems and limited resources for prevention and care fuel the spread of the virus.

High-income countries

During the year 2000, 30,000 adults and children are estimated to have acquired HIV in Western Europe, and 45,000 in North America. Overall HIV prevalence has risen slightly in both regions, mainly because anti retroviral therapy is keeping HIV-positive people alive longer.

Sub-Saharan Africa

In Africa south of the Sahara desert, an estimated 3.8 million adults and children became infected with HIV

during the year 2000, bringing the total number of people in the region living with HIV/AIDS to 25.3 million by the end of the year. The number of people who became infected during the year was slightly less than the 1999 total of 4.0 million. However, this trend will not continue if countries such as Nigeria begin experiencing a rapid expansion.

For the moment, overall HIV prevalence, the regional total of people living with HIV or AIDS, continues to rise because there are still more newly infected individuals joining it each year than there are people leaving it through death. However, as people infected years ago succumb to HIV-related illnesses (average survival in the absence of anti retroviral therapy is estimated at around 8-10 years), mortality from AIDS is increasing. AIDS deaths in 2000 totalled 2.4 million, as compared with 2.2 million in 1999. In the coming years, unless there is far broader access to life-prolonging therapy, and providing that new infections do not start rising again, the number of surviving HIV-positive Africans can be expected to stabilise and finally shrink, as AIDS increasingly claims the lives of those infected long ago.

It is estimated that between 12 and 13 African women are currently infected for every 10 African men. There are a number of reasons why female prevalence is higher than male in this region, including the greater efficiency of male-to-female HIV transmission through sex and the younger age at initial infection for women.

Eastern Europe and Central Asia
The estimated number of adults and children living with HIV or AIDS in Eastern Europe and the countries of the former Soviet Union was 420,000 at the end of 1999. Just one year later, a conservative estimate puts the figure at 700,000. Most of the quarter-million adults who became infected during 2000 are men, the majority of them injecting drug users. During the year new epidemics in drug injectors emerged in Uzbekistan and in Estonia, a country which reported far more HIV cases in 2000 than in any previous year.

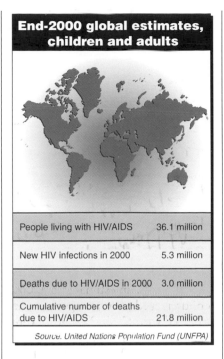

End-2000 global estimates, children and adults

People living with HIV/AIDS	36.1 million
New HIV infections in 2000	5.3 million
Deaths due to HIV/AIDS in 2000	3.0 million
Cumulative number of deaths due to HIV/AIDS	21.8 million

Source. United Nations Population Fund (UNFPA)

HIV shows no sign of curbing its exponential growth in the Russian Federation. Judging from the number of cases reported during the first nine months of the year, registered new infections during the year 2000 may well reach 50,000. This is far more than the total of 29,000 infections registered in the country between 1987 and 1999. However, even this massive rise understates the real growth in the epidemic: by Russian estimates, the national registration system captures just a fraction of the infections. Unsafe drug-injecting practices are still the major spur to HIV transmission in this huge nation.

Asia
An estimated 700,000 adults, 450,000 of them men, have become infected in South and South-East Asia in the course of the year 2000. Overall, as of end 2000, the region is estimated to have 5.8 million adults and children living with HIV or AIDS.

The region of East Asia and the Pacific is still keeping HIV at bay in most of its huge population. Some 130,000 adults and children became infected in the course of the year. This brings the number of people living with HIV or AIDS at the end of the year 2000 to 640,000, representing just 0.07% of the region's adult population, as compared with the prevalence rate of 0.56% in South and South-East Asia.

North Africa and the Middle East
Few new country estimates of HIV infection were produced for this region between 1994 and 1999. Recent evidence, however, suggests that new infections are on the rise. With an estimated 80,000 new infections in the region during 2000, the number of adults and children living with HIV or AIDS had reached 400,000 by the end of the year 2000.

Latin America and the Caribbean
In Latin America an estimated 150,000 adults and children became infected during 2000. By the end of the year some 1.4 million adults and children in the region were estimated to be living with HIV or AIDS, as compared with 1.3 million at the end of 1999.

The future
What is needed on a massive national and international level is to:
- end the stifling silence that continues to surround HIV in many countries,
- explode myths and misconceptions that translate into dangerous sexual practices,
- expand prevention initiatives such as condom promotion that can reduce sexual transmission,
- create conditions in which young children have the knowledge and the emotional and financial support to grow up free of HIV,
- devote real money to providing care for those infected with HIV and support to their families.
- A trail of successful responses has already been blazed by a small number of dedicated communities and governments. The challenge for everyone is to adapt and massively expand successful approaches that make it harder for the virus to spread, and that make it easier for those affected to live full and rewarding lives.

Source: UNAIDS Joint United Nations Programme on HIV/AIDS, 'AIDS Epidemic Update December 2000' and 'Report on the global HIV/AIDS epidemic June 2000'.

- The above information is from AVERT's web site which can be found at www.avert.org

© AVERT

HIV and AIDS

Frequently asked questions

Where can HIV be found? Which bodily fluids contain HIV?

HIV is present in infectious quantities in:

- Blood and blood products
- Semen and possibly pre-cum
- Vaginal and cervical secretions
- Breast milk

During invasive surgical procedures healthcare workers may also come into contact with the following bodily fluids, which contain significant amounts of HIV:

- Amniotic fluid
- Cerebrospinal fluid
- Synovial fluid around bone joints

HIV is present in negligible quantities in:

- Saliva (only found in minute amounts in a very small number of people)
- Tears
- Blister fluid

HIV is not present in:

- Urine
- Faeces
- Vomit
- Sweat

How long can HIV survive outside the human body?

Generally the fragile nature of the virus prevents it from surviving for a substantial amount of time in the open air.

The only studies on the survival of HIV outside the body have been conducted in the laboratory under controlled scientific conditions. These studies have found HIV is not affected by extreme cold, but it is destroyed by temperatures of 60 degrees centigrade and above.

Scientific studies have found that HIV can sometimes survive in dried blood at room temperature for up to six days. It is extremely difficult to assess exactly the length of survival of HIV outside the body in a non-laboratory setting.

Is there any way that HIV can create itself?

HIV cannot create itself under any

circumstances. The virus has to be present in a person's body and then passed on to someone else. HIV does not develop in a person's body of its own accord like for example cancer. HIV is a transmissible infection, which is passed from one person to another.

The only way that a person can become infected with HIV is if the bodily fluids of an infected person get into the body of an uninfected person.

The main ways in which HIV transmission takes place are through unprotected anal or vaginal sexual intercourse i.e. sex without a condom. Through blood-to-blood contact, usually infection in this way is the result of sharing needles with an infected person. Finally infection may take place from an infected mother to her child either in the womb, at birth or through breast-feeding.

How safe is oral sex?

Although it is possible to become infected with HIV through oral sex,

the risk of becoming infected in this way is much lower than the risk of infection via unprotected sexual intercourse with a man or woman.

When giving oral sex to a man (sucking or licking a man's penis) a person could become infected with HIV if infected semen got into any cuts, sores or receding gums a person might have in their mouth.

Giving oral sex to a woman (licking a woman's clitoris or vagina) is also considered relatively low risk. Transmission could take place if infected sexual fluids from a woman got into the mouth of her partner. The likelihood of infection occurring might be increased if there is menstrual blood involved or the woman is infected with another STD.

The likelihood of either a man or a woman becoming infected with HIV as a consequence of receiving oral sex is extremely low.

What are the chances of becoming infected with HIV if he doesn't come inside me?

Whilst research suggests that high concentrations of HIV can sometimes be detected in pre-cum, it difficult to judge whether HIV is present in sufficient quantities for infection to occur. To guard against the possibility of infection with HIV

or any other STD it is best to practise safer sex i.e. sex with a condom.

Is deep kissing a route of HIV transmission?

Deep or open-mouthed kissing is a very low risk activity in terms of HIV transmission. HIV is only present in saliva in very minute amounts, insufficient to cause infection with HIV alone.

There has been only one documented case of someone becoming infected with HIV through kissing; a result of exposure to infected blood during open-mouthed kissing. If you or your partner have blood in your mouth, you should avoid kissing until the bleeding stops.

Can I become infected with HIV through normal social contact/activities such as shaking hands/toilet seats/swimming pools/sharing cutlery/kissing/sneezes and coughs?

No. This is because HIV is not an airborne, water-borne or food-borne virus. Also, the virus does not survive for very long outside the human body. Therefore ordinary social contact such as kissing, shaking hands, coughing and sharing cutlery does not result in the virus being passed from one person to another.

Can I become infected with HIV from needles on movie/cinema seats?

There have been a number of stories circulating via the Internet and e-mail, about people becoming infected from needles left on cinema seats and in coin-return slots. However, these rumours appear to have no factual basis.

For HIV infection to take place in this way the needle would need to contain infected blood with a high level of infectious virus. If a person was then pricked with an infected needle, they could become infected although there is only a 0.4% chance.

Although discarded needles can transfer blood and blood-borne illnesses such as hepatitis B, C and HIV, the risk of infection taking place in this way is extremely low.

Is there a risk of HIV transmission when having a tattoo, body piercing or visiting the barber's?

If instruments contaminated with

The only way that a person can become infected with HIV is if the bodily fluids of an infected person get into the body of an uninfected person

---

blood are not sterilised between clients there is a risk of HIV transmission. However, people who carry out body piercing or tattoos should follow procedures called 'universal precautions', which are designed to prevent the transmission of blood-borne infections such as HIV and hepatitis B.

When visiting the barber's there is no risk of infection unless the skin is cut and infected blood gets into the wound. Traditional 'cut-throat' razors used by barbers now have disposable blades, which should only be used once, and so reduce the risk of blood-borne infections such as hepatitis and HIV.

Am I at risk of becoming infected with HIV when visiting the doctor's or dentist's?

Transmission of HIV in a healthcare setting is extremely rare. All health professionals are required to follow infection control procedures when caring for any patient. These procedures are called universal precautions for infection control. They are designed to protect both patients and healthcare professionals from the transmission of blood-borne diseases such as hepatitis B and HIV.

Can I become infected with HIV through biting?

Infection with HIV in this way is unusual. There have only been a couple of documented cases of HIV transmission resulting from biting. In these particular cases, severe tissue tearing and damage were reported in addition to the presence of blood.

Can I get HIV from a mosquito?

No, it is not possible to get HIV from mosquitoes. When taking blood from someone mosquitoes do not inject blood from any previous person. The only thing that a mosquito injects is saliva, which acts as a lubricant and enables it to feed more efficiently.

If blood splashes into my eye can I become infected with HIV?

Research suggests the risk of HIV infection in this way is extremely small. A very small number of people – usually in a healthcare setting – have become infected with HIV as a result of blood splashes in the eye.

What are the main routes of HIV transmission?

These are the main ways in which someone can become infected with HIV:

- Unprotected penetrative intercourse with someone who is infected.
- Injection or transfusion of contaminated blood or blood products, donations of semen (artificial insemination), skin grafts and organ transplants taken from someone who is infected.
- From a mother who is infected to her baby; this may be during the course of pregnancy, at birth and through breast-feeding.
- Sharing unsterilised injection equipment that has been previously used by someone who is infected.

Would I know whether I was infected with HIV if I got tested straight away?

Infection with HIV has no specific symptoms. The only way you can find out for sure if you are infected with HIV is by taking the HIV antibody test.

The HIV antibody test looks for antibodies to the virus in a person's blood. For most people these antibodies take 3 months to develop, with 98% having developed antibodies within six months of infection.

Getting tested before the 3-month period is up may result in an unclear test result, as an infected person may not have developed antibodies to HIV yet. So it is best to wait for at least 3 months after the last time you were at risk before taking the test. Some test centres may recommend testing again at 6 months, just to be extra sure.

It is also important that you are not at risk of further exposures to HIV during this time period. Most importantly you should continue to practise safe sex and not share needles.

What are the first symptoms of HIV infection?

The only way to know for sure whether you are infected with HIV is to have an HIV antibody test.

The symptoms of initial HIV infection are not very specific. If a person is infected, a few weeks after infection some people experience a flu-like illness. Only a fifth of people experience symptoms which are serious enough to require a doctor's attention.

Several years after infection a person may experience symptoms of particular illnesses and cancers. These are the result of the infected person's immune system being

---

You cannot tell whether a person is infected with HIV or has developed AIDS by how they look and appear to you

---

damaged by HIV to the point where it is no longer able to fight off these opportunistic infections.

In each case, HIV infection is difficult to diagnose without having taken an HIV antibody test first.

How do I know if I have AIDS?

You cannot tell whether a person is infected with HIV or has developed AIDS by how they look and appear to you.

A person infected with HIV is diagnosed as having AIDS when

---

they develop an AIDS defining illness. This is the result of HIV weakening their immune system to the point at which it has difficulty fighting off infections that would otherwise be controlled by a healthy immune system. Because these illnesses take advantage of an infected person's immune system to cause illness, they are also know as opportunistic infections.

In many countries anti-viral drugs are available to people with HIV to help reduce the rate at which HIV weakens the immune system. There are also drugs available to prevent and treat some of the specific opportunistic infections.

• The above information is from AVERT's web site which can be found at www.avert.org Alternatively, see page 41 for their address details.

© AVERT

---

40 per cent rise in Aids feared over next three years

The number of people diagnosed with Aids in England and Wales is expected to rise by 40 per cent in the next three years.

Issuing the figures to coincide with World Aids Day today, the Public Health Laboratory Service said that there were more than 3,000 new cases last year in England and Wales, a record annual number of diagnoses.

By 2003 there would be 29,000 people in the country with HIV, compared with 20,800 at the beginning of this year, it said. Improved drug treatments save lives but mean that there are more people capable of transmitting the disease.

Dr Barry Evans, a consultant at the laboratory service, said: 'It is important to remember that although we have drugs that can help prevent the progression of HIV disease, we have no cure. So prevention must remain the key to tackling this infection. We cannot afford to be complacent about HIV. People must heed the safer sex messages.'

By Celia Hall, Medical Editor

Homosexual men remain the group at greatest risk of HIV infection, although the proportion of heterosexual people continues to rise. In 1990, 22 per cent of new diagnoses were in heterosexuals. By 1999 this was 48 per cent. Most infections in heterosexual men were acquired abroad, 65 per cent in Africa.

Many more people have the infection but do not know it, a report by the Department of Health said yesterday. Complacency about HIV and Aids and ignorance of whether they were infected was particularly high among heterosexuals, the report found.

Yvette Cooper, the health minister, announced an allocation of £41 million for health authorities in England to treat and care for people with Aids. A Mori poll of more than 2,000 people found that despite multi-million-pound campaigns many people were ignorant about the risks of becoming infected.

One in 10 people wrongly believed that there was a cure for Aids. A further one in 10 were unsure. A quarter of people said they did not know enough about their risk of becoming infected. About three million people will die from Aids throughout the world this year.

© *Telegraph Group Limited, London 2001*

General information: HIV

This article gives basic, non-technical information on HIV infection. The information may be especially useful for those teaching about sexual health or preparing projects on sexually transmitted infections

What is HIV and what does it do?

- HIV stands for human immunodeficiency virus.

- There are two types of HIV virus: HIV-1 and HIV-2. HIV-1 is the type most commonly found in the UK. HIV-2 remains mainly confined to West Africa and is usually less severe than HIV-1.

- When a person has HIV, infectious amounts of the virus can be found in their blood, semen (men), vaginal fluids (women) and breast milk (women).

- People with HIV usually have no symptoms for a prolonged period of time, while the virus acts slowly to weaken the body's immune system. HIV particularly attacks the type of white blood cell called CD4 cells. When the CD4 count is very low the body's immune system is very weak.

- When a person's immune system has been broken down he or she is susceptible to other illnesses, especially infections (e.g. tuberculosis and pneumonia) and cancers, many of which are not normally a threat to a healthy person.

- At that severe stage of infection the person is often diagnosed as having AIDS. AIDS stands for acquired immunodeficiency syndrome.

- To say that a person has AIDS means they have one or more of a list of otherwise usually rare illnesses as a result of the breakdown of the body's immune system.

- Usually the cause of illness and eventual death in a person with HIV is not the virus itself, but illnesses to which the virus has made the person vulnerable. With treatment a person with AIDS may recover from an illness, but will usually succumb to another. People with HIV infection will almost certainly die prematurely.

- Recent advances in treatment by combination anti-retroviral therapy (sometimes called Highly Active Anti-Retroviral Therapy or HAART) have enormously improved survival rates in countries which can afford these drugs and have the infrastructure to deliver them safely and effectively.

Who gets HIV?

- Anyone can become infected with the virus if he or she is exposed to infection through sex or blood products.

- There are certain groups at higher risk of infection than others in the UK:
  – Homosexual men (men who have sex with men)
  – Injecting drug users
  – Men and women who have lived as adults in countries where heterosexual transmission of HIV is common (notably South, East and Central Africa)
  – Children, from their infected mothers during pregnancy

- The numbers of HIV infections acquired through sex between men and women are low in the UK but represent 80-90% of infections worldwide.

- In 2000 there were over 3,400 reports of new diagnoses of HIV infection in the UK. Nearly 40% of these were in men who probably acquired their infection through sex with another man. Almost half acquired their infection heterosexually and about 3% through injecting drug use. Most of the heterosexuals were probably infected abroad.

In 2000 there were over 3,400 reports of new diagnoses of HIV infection in the UK

- HIV is uncommon among young heterosexual people in the UK and fewer than 1 in 1000 UK-born teenagers attending STD clinics (generally a higher risk group) were infected with HIV in 1999. Among young sexually active people in the UK, homosexual young men are at greater risk than heterosexuals.

- For heterosexual teenagers the risk of catching chlamydia, gonorrhoea or another sexually transmitted infection is far higher than the risk of catching HIV. Those infected with another sexually transmitted infection are at a higher risk of acquiring HIV if they have an HIV-infected partner.

How do you catch HIV?

- HIV is passed on from an infected person through the transfer of body fluids such as blood, semen, fluid from the woman's cervix and breast milk.

- There are four main ways to catch HIV:
  – By unprotected sexual intercourse (anal, vaginal or oral) with an infected partner. Anal intercourse (where a man's penis is inserted into his partner's anus) is more dangerous than vaginal intercourse. This is because the lining of the anus is easily damaged. The lining of the vagina and skin in general, if undamaged, is relatively resistant to HIV. The virus is passed on more readily from men to women than from women to men. The risk associated with unprotected oral sex is lower than other forms of penetrative sex, but is not risk free.
  – By an injection or transfusion with blood from an infected person.
  – Through drug users sharing needles and syringes contaminated with HIV-infected blood.

– From an infected mother to her baby during birth or through breast-feeding.

- HIV is NOT passed on through everyday social contact with an infected person. Touching, shaking hands, hugging, coughing or sneezing cannot pass on the virus.
- Not everyone who comes into contact with the virus will contract it. For example, most babies born to HIV-positive mothers are not infected with the virus.

How do you know that you have HIV?

- A person with HIV may have no symptoms and appear completely healthy for a long period of time.
- Antibodies are complex proteins made by the body's immune system against 'foreign' substances such as bacteria and viruses. There is a test that can be done on a blood sample which will detect the presence of antibodies to HIV. Someone with HIV antibodies is infected with the virus (but transfer of mother's antibodies to new-born babies occurs even though the baby is not necessarily infected).
- It can take up to 3 months for the antibodies to show up in a test after the person was infected. However, during that interval the infected person will have high numbers of the virus in his or her body, and will be likely to pass on infection at this stage if they have unprotected sexual intercourse.

How serious is HIV?

- HIV is a serious infection in the UK where it is estimated that around 30,000 people are currently infected. Without treatment most people are expected to die from their infection.
- Once infected with HIV the person carries the virus in their body for the rest of their lives and remains infectious to others for the rest of their lives. However, recent treatment advances mean that in treated patients the virus level can be reduced but these treatments need to be maintained and there is not as yet a cure for HIV.

- At the end of 2000, there were more than 36.1 million people living with HIV infection worldwide, over 95% of these in resource-poor (developing) countries.

How can you protect yourself against HIV?

- Sexually active men and women greatly reduce their risk of infection by having monogamous relationships with HIV-negative partners.
- A condom is a form of contraception that if used correctly and consistently during sexual intercourse can protect against HIV.
- Even in an entirely monogamous relationship one partner may bring HIV, or another infection, from a previous partner without having any symptoms.
- Injecting drug users should never share their needles, syringes and other injecting equipment with anyone else. This will minimise their risk of catching HIV (and other viral infections, hepatitis B and C). Used needles should be disposed of safely by putting them in a rigid container with a lid. There are now needle exchange programmes in many parts of the country which provide free supplies of clean, sterile needles and safely dispose of used needles.
- Since 1985 all blood donated for medical transfusions has been screened for HIV, meaning there is minimal risk of being infected through a hospital blood transfusion.
- HIV-positive mothers can be put on special antiviral medication to reduce the risk of transmission of HIV to the baby during birth. They should not breast-feed, as the virus can be transmitted via breast milk.

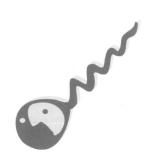

How is HIV diagnosed?

- The main test for HIV infection is the blood test for antibodies to HIV described under 'How do you know you have HIV?'
- Confidential HIV tests can be obtained from any STD clinic (also called genitourinary medicine clinics) or GP. Details of these clinics can be found in the telephone book, from your local hospital or from the STD clinic index of the Health Development Agency's sexual health web site. You can attend at any age (even if you are below the legal age of consent to sex which is 16).
- There is complete confidentiality between the person tested and the doctor responsible for the test. This covers the fact that a test has been taken and the result of that test.

Can you treat HIV?

- Currently there is no vaccine or cure for HIV.
- However, there is now treatment called highly active antiretroviral treatment (HAART). The treatment suppresses the HIV virus and can reverse the damage to the immune system for some time, prolonging the lives of those infected. The virus is continually changing, sometimes becoming resistant to current drugs, so HAART may not be a long-term solution and it is not a cure.
- People can only be prescribed these drugs if they have been tested and know that they have the infection
- The treatments are complex and often have side effects. They are not easy to take.
- Treatment is also very expensive and therefore unavailable to most people in the developing countries.
- Despite treatment an infected person is still capable of passing on the virus.

• The above information is an extract from the Public Health Laboratory Service's web site which can be found at www.phls.co.uk

© *Public Health Laboratory Service (PHLS)*

Young men and HIV

Information from the United Nations Programme on HIV/ AIDS (UNAIDS) and the Panos Institute 2001

Of all men and women and across all age groups, it is among young men aged between 15 and 24 where the riskiest attitudes and behaviour relating to HIV can be found – from drug injection and multiple sexual partners, through to unprotected sex between men.

With the 2000/2001 World AIDS Campaign focusing on men, it is now fairly well known that the behaviour and attitudes of men of all ages drive the epidemic. This is because men tend to have more sexual partners than women, and are likely to hold the power in sexual relations – determining, for example, when sex should take place and whether a condom should be used.

However, there is very little awareness of the extent to which young men are a key component of this driving force, both in terms of their present and their future roles in spreading HIV.

Young people account for 60 per cent of new HIV infections. We do not know exactly what proportion of all HIV infections are among young men. Most information about the rates of infection comes from antenatal testing and therefore does not give specific information about young men. We know that in parts of Africa, young women are up to five times more likely to be infected than young men. However, worldwide, men still account for more HIV infections than women and it is likely that young men make up a significant proportion of this number.

According to the Joint United Nations Programme on HIV/AIDS (UNAIDS), young men under 25 currently account for up to a quarter of the world's people living with HIV.[1] The fact that this age group, spanning only nine years, makes up such a large proportion of those infected is a grave indication of their significance in the spread of the virus.

Not only do young men represent a large part of the popula-tion, but as they mature they will play a key role in the future of the epidemic. This is partly through their attitudes and behaviour today, but also because as individuals in their private lives and as leaders respons-ible for the communities in which they live, they will influence the response to the epidemic in the future. (Ideally, both men and women should lead communities and nations; in practice men will have greater power in most societies for the foreseeable future.)

Missing out

Given the fact that young men account for so many of those living with HIV and practise so many forms of behaviour that create HIV risk, it is surprising that there are relatively few services or interventions designed with them in mind. There are also relatively few studies on their attitudes or sexual behaviour.

At a meeting on the Health and Development of African Young Men, co-ordinated by the World Health Organisation (WHO) in 2000, there was a general consensus that not nearly enough work was being done with young men. It was acknow-ledged that services for adolescents either target young people in general, or just young women. Young men as a group in their own right are given very little attention.

This is the case even in Latin America, where there are propor-tionately more services for young men than elsewhere. Seventeen organisations participating in a survey co-ordinated by WHO noted that services for adolescent males were scarce and under-resourced.[2] Furthermore, government support for these services was often not forth-coming and most of the funds came from private international agencies. 'These programmes echoed a

What about boys?

This report focuses on young men aged 15–24, but there is also a real need to provide HIV information and education – and in some circumstances clinical services – to boys below this age.

Boys aged 10 to 14 are still considered children. However, many boys below the age of 15 are already sexually active. Four out of 10 Jamaican boys have had sex before the age of 15. One-third of American and Brazilian boys have had intercourse by this age, along with one-quarter of boys from Costa Rica and the Dominican Republic.[5] One study estimates that more than half of the world's population have had unprotected sex (sex without a condom) before the age of 16.[6]

However old they are when they start having sex, attitudes towards sexuality and women are formed from an early age. So although most risky behaviour is found among young men over 15, this is often shaped in the younger years. And helping boys learn about relationships and sex before these relationships begin is the best time to influence them.

This does not mean that young boys have the same needs as adult men in their early twenties. Sexual health information programmes for boys below the age of 15 need to be sensitive to local cultural ideas about youth and sexuality, while also engaging realistically with adolescent needs.

One of the obstacles to broader AIDS-related programmes for children and teenagers is the idea that sex and AIDS education can lead to increased sexual activity. A number of studies have shown that the opposite is more likely to be the case.[7] Regardless of the moral debates around early sexual activity, it is clear that these young people should at least have the knowledge necessary to protect themselves.

common refrain that policymakers at the national and local levels have not recognised the special need of adolescent males,'[3] according to the survey.

In another case, an international development agency ran a survey on the sexual health programmes it was funding in the developing world. These programmes – considered to be progressive in terms of male involvement – reported that only 25 per cent of clients were male, and only 10 per cent of funds were allocated to working with men.[4]

One key reason why young men have been overlooked in the response to HIV lies in the history of reproductive health programming. Most reproductive health services – which until recently represented a large part of the health infrastructure dealing with HIV/AIDS – are run by and mainly cater for women. In the past, sexual and reproductive health was centred on family planning and was considered a female domain. But with the emergence of the AIDS pandemic, including men became an urgent necessity. Recognising this fact, the 1994 International Conference on Population and Development made a number of clear and high-profile statements on the need to increase male involvement. Despite this, the basic fact remains: the needs of young men and their roles in the epidemic are poorly understood and given relatively little attention in HIV/AIDS programming.

Roles and attitudes

Young men do not seem to represent a particularly vulnerable group. They do not easily evoke feelings of sympathy and compassion. Often their expressions of frustration and marginalisation discourage those in the community who might be able to offer assistance. When we are insulted on the street, or mugged, or worse, the chances are that the perpetrator will be a young man, or – more likely – a group of young men. And popular notions of masculinity mean that boys are not supposed to cry, or to complain about their suffering. So the fact that society is often victim to the actions of young men who outwardly seem tough and

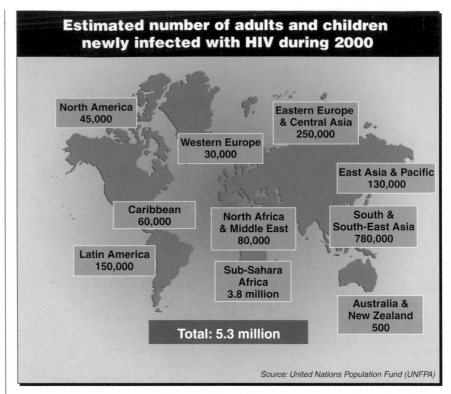

Estimated number of adults and children newly infected with HIV during 2000

North America 45,000

Eastern Europe & Central Asia 250,000

Western Europe 30,000

East Asia & Pacific 130,000

Caribbean 60,000

North Africa & Middle East 80,000

South & South-East Asia 780,000

Latin America 150,000

Sub-Sahara Africa 3.8 million

Australia & New Zealand 500

Total: 5.3 million

Source: United Nations Population Fund (UNFPA)

aggressive means notions of vulnerability and neediness do not easily fit.

'Provided you have no job, people will say you are "mwezi" (thief). Youth are considered a bad group in society, especially those who have no jobs. Society does not respect them.'
20-year-old man,
Dar es Salaam[8]

'I think boys never become men . . . never become responsible. They just grow up and become hairy . . . They mature little. Even with experience, they always have their childish part.'
Adolescent woman,
Rio de Janeiro, Brazil[9]

It is also important to note that while some elements of masculinity can create risks from HIV, other elements actually protect against the virus. For example, many young men aspire to become fathers at some point in their lives. In many cultures fatherhood implies responsibility and care – attributes that could be channelled into HIV prevention. Other common masculine ideals that can form the building blocks for change include the idea that men have to physically protect their partners and the concept that young men have to be physically fit (and therefore free from disease).

Assertiveness, free-thinking, teamwork and the willingness to fight for what is right are also associated with what it means to be a man in many parts of the world. All these are masculine ideals that can be harnessed in the fight against AIDS.

If young men are to be included in the response to HIV, then their views need to be heard. This will ensure interventions are appropriate to this particular group, and will also help the young men take ownership of the AIDS problem and help keep them as partners in the response. That means that when new approaches that involve young men in the response to AIDS are designed, young men must be given a voice in all stages of the process. They often have very clear views about what should be done to help them protect themselves and their partners.

The AIDS Committee of the South African Youth Council and male representatives from an AIDS Committee of the Kenyan Mathare Youth Sports Association listed a number of priority issues for policymakers to address.

'Help create more jobs'
Poverty and lack of opportunity as a major obstacle in changing attitudes and behaviour relating to HIV/AIDS.

'Make youth more HIV/AIDS conscious'

Information and education are a top priority.

'Teach young men to help themselves because this is not only a government problem. Assist us in our own fight against HIV/AIDS'

Young men, along with young women, have a right to determine their own futures. Programmes for young people should empower both to take ownership of the struggle against HIV/AIDS.

'Seek youth development by providing a youth desk in every local government office'

Young men are often marginalised from larger systems of power and decision-making. Practical and democratic measures should be taken to ensure that young people are given a voice in government.

'Build more youth counselling centres in the communities'

Young men and women need HIV/AIDS services, which can cater for their needs. Young men have been excluded from such services due to their gender and life stage.

'Start teaching about AIDS in our school curriculum – in a language understood by the youth'

In many countries, school education on HIV/AIDS and sexual health does not address the needs of young people. Young men want clear guidelines on sexual health issues.

Don't forget young women

The focus on HIV/AIDS and other gender and reproductive health issues must be expanded to include young men but clearly in no way should resources or attention be diverted from protecting young women from HIV.

This point can hardly be stressed enough because for years those working in the area of women's rights and reproductive health have fought for improvements in the lives of women. This battle has involved raising awareness and highlighting the way that different societies and cultures perpetuate the power relations that disadvantage women. The battle is still being fought and, although real progress has been made, countless women around the world still suffer discrimination and disadvantage in every aspect of their lives.

Any argument for broadening the response to HIV to include young men needs to begin with acknowledging that young women are far more vulnerable than young men to HIV/AIDS. Their bodies offer less physiological resistance to contracting HIV, and socially their status and gender roles put them at greater risk from the virus. In sub-Saharan Africa, the HIV infection rate among teenage girls is five times the rate among teenage boys.

There must be no sense, then, that a focus on young men detracts from the focus on young women. There can be no competition between men and women, but a shared struggle for the rights of both. In Latin America, where services targeting young men are relatively developed, some organisations avoid the issue of competition between programming for boys and programming for girls by presenting both within a unified gender approach – helping them understand that their attitudes and behaviour towards each other are frequently determined by the gender roles that society imposes.[10]

Gender theory – why men and women behave the way they do – has informed the women's rights movement throughout and has developed in line with contemporary social change. These developments include a new focus on 'what makes a man' – looking at the components of masculinity and how they are learned. Looking at men in this way makes it possible to understand their behaviour towards women and also to consider the challenges that men face.

The AIDS pandemic has focused international attention on these issues particularly as they relate to sexual risk. And with this new focus has come the recognition that many ideas of 'masculinity' not only put women at risk from HIV, but greatly disadvantage men as well.

Notes

1 *Men and AIDS, A Gendered Approach* World AIDS Campaign 2000 UNAIDS March 2000, p8
2 *WHO Survey on Programs Working with Adolescent Boys and Young Men*, Summary Report Latin America, Caribbean, US G Barker, WHO 1998
3 As note 2
4 *Involving Men in Reproductive Health Activities* – A review of USAID funded activities N Danforth and C P Green, Population Technical Assistance Project (POPTECH) 1997 Arlington, Virginia, p13
5 Gender Differences in the Timing of First Intercourse: Data from 14 Countries Susheela Singh, Deirdre Wulf, Renee Samara and Yvette P Cuca, *International Family Planning Perspectives*, Vol 26, No 1, June 2000
6 *Policy Paper on HIV/AIDS*, Save the Children Fund [Unpublished 2000]
7 *Effects of Sex Education on Young People's Sexual Behaviour*. Geneva, Anne Grunseit and Susan Kippax, 1993: World Health Organisation, Office of Intervention, Development and Support, Global Programme on AIDS
8 Michelle Sheldrake, personal communication with the author. Quotes collected during fieldwork in Dar es Salaam, Tanzania, 2000, Key Centre for Women's Health in Society, University of Melbourne, Australia
9 Where the boys are: Attitudes related to masculinity, fatherhood and violence toward women among low income adolescent and young adult males in Rio de Janeiro, Brazil G Barker and I Loewenstein, *Youth and Society*, 1997, 29/2, pp166-96
10 As note 2

• The above information is an extract from the report *Young men and HIV*, produced jointly by the United Nations Programme on HIV/AIDS (UNAIDS) and The Panos Institute 2001

What happens when someone has HIV?

Information from the Terrence Higgins Trust

Most people who become infected with HIV do not notice that they have been infected. A few weeks after infection, the body's immune system reacts to the virus by producing antibodies. Some people with HIV have a short 'seroconversion' illness at the time these antibodies are created. The likely symptoms are the normal response to many other infections, and may include a sore throat, a fever or a rash.

Someone living with HIV will have their CD4 count and viral load regularly monitored by means of simple blood tests. The results of these tests vary in response to infections, stress, exercise and the time of day, but it is of primary importance in indicating how their health is holding up under the assault of HIV. When someone has lived with HIV for a long time and their immune system has been severely damaged, there is a risk of opportunistic infections. Increasingly, it is possible to prevent or treat opportunistic infections, which may arise in someone living with HIV using drugs.

For example, Pneumocistis carinii pneumonia (PCP) was a frequent cause of death in people with AIDS or late stage infection in the early years of the epidemic. Doctors are now able to prevent PCP with drugs, or to treat it quickly if it occurs. Death from PCP is now rare among people with HIV in the UK.

The most effective way to attack HIV is with a combination of anti-HIV drugs. Combination therapy is a huge advance in the treatment of HIV, and many people have done very well on it. Combination therapy is not a cure for HIV and, because of complex rules governing how the drugs need to be taken, various drug regimens can be difficult to take or adhere to. But combination therapy has greatly reduced the number of people dying from HIV. As a consequence of combination therapy, today in Europe five times fewer people are dying of HIV infection than in 1995.

The real problems

Even though there are now more powerful anti-HIV treatments, which can suppress the progress of HIV infection, living with the knowledge of a serious and potentially life-threatening infection can be stressful and difficult. Someone with HIV may remain in good physical health for several years but misunderstandings and fears about HIV are still widespread in society. People living with the virus may encounter hostility or rejection even from friends and family. Some have lost jobs and homes due to their employers' or landlords' attitudes, and children with HIV have been banned from schools.

Many people with HIV have seen friends and partners become ill before them, and may have seen them die. Some communities have been particularly affected by HIV; for example, gay men, people from sub-

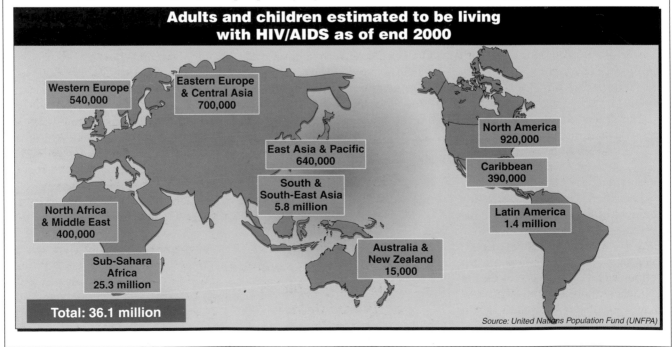

Adults and children estimated to be living with HIV/AIDS as of end 2000

Western Europe 540,000

Eastern Europe & Central Asia 700,000

East Asia & Pacific 640,000

South & South-East Asia 5.8 million

North Africa & Middle East 400,000

Sub-Sahara Africa 25.3 million

Australia & New Zealand 15,000

North America 920,000

Caribbean 390,000

Latin America 1.4 million

Total: 36.1 million

Source: United Nations Population Fund (UNFPA)

Saharan Africa and injecting drug-users. In some parts of the world, and among some African communities in the UK, it is not unusual for whole families to die from HIV.

Many HIV positive people choose to tell no one about their diagnosis except for a few trusted friends, and this burden of secrecy can be very hard to bear. Living with the knowledge that you could pass a serious infection to someone else can also be very hard. A number of support groups have been set up around the country to help counter the isolation which HIV can cause and to help people make changes in their lives to cope with living with HIV.

HIV in the world

Of the 33.4 million people infected with HIV around the world in 1999, there are estimated to be 22.5 million in sub-Saharan Africa, 6.7 million in South and South-east Asia, 1.4 million in Latin America and 0.7 million in the USA. There are about 9,000 new infections each day, 90% of which occur in developing countries. Globally, more than 14 million people have died of the disease, including 2.5 million in 1998.

For most people with HIV, recent advances in the treatment of HIV will have little impact. The high cost of developing and producing new drugs and the lack of available funds for healthcare in many countries make it unlikely that the new therapies will ever be widely available in the developing world. For future control of the epidemic in both developed and developing countries, an effective preventative vaccine is essential. It would not help those already infected with HIV, but it would reduce future infections.

Throughout the world, roughly equal numbers of men and women are infected. But HIV mainly affects young adults and people in early middle age. These are the people who raise the children, support the elderly and build a country's economy. This loss has already had a serious effect on the economies of countries in sub-Saharan Africa and may well affect other countries in the future.

Stopping the epidemic

We could slow down the worldwide HIV epidemic if everyone had the information they need about preventing infection, and had society's support to help them act on this information. For example, young men growing up gay need access to good information about how to avoid becoming infected with HIV. Gay men who were sexually active when the first publicity appeared warning against AIDS are aware of the risks of unprotected sex. But each new generation of gay men needs to be made aware of the risks of HIV.

In countries like the UK with forward-thinking programmes for injecting drug users, including needle exchange projects and methadone schemes, rates of HIV among drug users are relatively low. In other countries, like Spain, France and the USA, HIV has spread rapidly because

Throughout the world, roughly equal numbers of men and women are infected. But HIV mainly affects young adults and people in early middle age

of public reluctance to protect the health of drug users.

Religious, cultural or economic restrictions can make it hard for people to use condoms and protect themselves and their partners. A woman who is economically dependent on a man may find it impossible to ask for safer sex. Worldwide, women are most commonly infected through unprotected sex with their husbands or long-term partners.

Denial by national leaders that some behaviours happen, such as sex between men or drug injecting, can make it particularly difficult for people to avoid the risks. Some governments do not accept that HIV is an issue for them at all.

People often react with prejudice and denial to things they do not understand. These reactions to HIV and AIDS hinder HIV prevention programmes, and they make life more difficult for people living with HIV. Every one of us can make a difference to the epidemic by fighting prejudice, challenging denial and increasing understanding.

• The above information is an extract from *HIV & AIDS – Understanding HIV infections and AIDS*, produced by the Terrence Higgins Trust. See page 41 for address details.

© Terrence Higgins Trust

Living with HIV

Learning you are HIV positive

Coping with and talking about the result

Scream, shout, cry, laugh, hide, run away, feel numb, scared, lonely, relieved. How did you think you would react to a positive result before you actually had the test? Were you right?

Reaction to the result is different for everyone. Over time, you'll find a way of dealing with it that suits you, but it might be quite different to the way other people cope with it. Try and think about living – thousands of other people live full and rewarding lives despite this virus, you can do it too.

Your first action as a person living with HIV is make a choice, what to do next. The choices won't stop there; making the right ones to enrich and extend your life might play an increasing part in every new day. This page is about giving you the choice to take control, make informed decisions, and get on with your life.

It's not easy

No one ever suggested any of this would be easy. If you need time and space to think your situation through, make it. Whatever you're going through is natural. How you deal with this news is up to you. HIV is threatening your existence, so it's all

right to be angry. If you are scared express your fears. Don't be hard on yourself and don't force yourself to be strong if you don't want to be.

Stress is natural and affects your emotions. Stress can help you to deal with some situations. However, excessive stress can cause physical symptoms, it can damage your immune system and make you ill. Take stock and find ways of managing the stress in your life. Find ways to relax and recharge your batteries. Listen to your body; if you are tired, rest and you'll be better for it.

Choose things that work for you

HIV can bring anxieties. One way of tackling this is through getting information, by learning about your condition, gaining confidence in it, in yourself and making informed choices for your future.

Alternatively, you might choose to ignore the diagnosis (but remember it won't go away) and just carry on with your life. It's your life, you choose.

You don't have to do anything. If you don't find that taking control works for you, fine. That's just as valid as any other approach

Do what works for you.

Getting information

Receiving a positive diagnosis, even if you were anticipating the result, is often very unsettling. As a result some people just accept the information they are given without really understanding it, or forget to ask questions essential for their peace of mind. However, being well informed about HIV and related issues can be vital and doctors, support organisations and other people living with HIV can all provide both advice and information.

Ultimately all decisions relating to your life will still be made by you, so if you are unclear about anything, for example the different side-effects of drug treatment, then ASK. Although the issues HIV raises can be surrounded by jargon, being assertive and getting informed can be as useful as any treatment

Who to tell?

Who is told, and how, can take a bit of thinking through. Telling close friends and family can provide enormous relief and support, but it can also cause problems. Do people

really need to know? Do they need to know immediately? Unfortunately, it's a fact of life that there's still a lot of stigma attached to an HIV diagnosis. Many people are still afraid of catching HIV through normal social contact. Your background or culture may also play a part in how difficult it might be for you to tell other people that you are HIV positive.

Who you tell and how you tell them will take a bit of thinking through. There can be advantages to talking openly about your status, but it could cause you problems. Be careful who you tell, don't rush off and tell everyone straight away – you might regret telling them later. Do they really have to know? If so, do they have to know now, or can you leave it till later? But sharing the news of your positive status with the right people can strengthen personal relationships and help you feel less isolated.

Probably the first thing that someone you tell will think about is how you got infected. If they're kind enough not to actually ask, be careful that they aren't making assumptions about you. For example, a positive heterosexual man is automatically assumed by many to be gay.

Talk to people you can trust, but try to make sure they will respect your need and right to confidentiality on this issue. Try to make sure whoever you discuss it with is sympathetic to your viewpoint, someone who won't judge you on your lifestyle, sexuality or being HIV positive.

This might be difficult, and though you think you know who your friends are, telling others about this might either confirm or damage personal relationships.

If you are gay, telling others about your status is like 'coming out' all over again. But if you haven't come out as gay, the extra news of HIV might be too much for whoever you tell to cope with. Drug users might have similar problems admitting to both drug use and HIV infection.

Are you prepared to deal with the concerns of people you tell; their panic, their tears on top of any

problems you might be having with your status at the moment?

However, some people find that being totally open about their status (never mind sexuality or drug use!) gives them great strength and lifts the burden of secrecy. Other people tell no one, but could be missing opportunities for support and care that disclosure might bring.

Disclosure could be where you find out who your friends really are. Carefully deciding who to tell might teach you how to deal with telling others

---

If you feel like just talking to someone, many people affected by HIV and AIDS are helped and supported by counselling sessions. AIDS organisations, telephone helplines, and many hospitals offer access to confidential and non-judgemental counselling.

Partner
Just as your HIV positive result was possibly a big event to happen in your life, if you're in a relationship the news will also have an impact on your partner. Consider the highly emotional aspects of revealing your status and, if possible, avoid the 'heat of the moment' to reveal all. No two relationships are the same, so it's difficult to give advice in this situation.

If you're going to tell, don't delay it for too long. If they are negative, or untested, they might resent you keeping it to yourself, adding unnecessary worry about any risk of infection they might have been in. Of course, if you discussed the issue before you were tested, talking through the result might be easier.

Previous partners
You'll probably need a lot of time to work this one through. Whether you tell depends on lots of things including whether you're still involved with them now, what they know about HIV, whether they're HIV positive or not themselves (and how do you find out?), and whether they need to know, perhaps because you had unsafe sex with them before you knew your status. How will either of you deal with worrying about who gave whom what?

Children
If you have children, you may have additional concerns about whether to tell them your diagnosis and whether they need to be tested too. Parents may well need to talk to someone with experience in this area – your clinic or local AIDS service organisation, or other parents with HIV might be able to help.

Friends
Disclosure could be where you find out who your friends really are. Carefully deciding who to tell might teach you how to deal with telling others. Common reactions are: shock, pity, disbelief, helplessness, or endless questions. Some people may decide they don't want to know or see you any more. But your real friends will carry on as before, liking and loving you for who you are, supporting you through any problems you have. Remember, being HIV positive does not stop you from being the person you were before you knew your test result.

Family
No two families are the same either. If your immediate family are supportive and loving, your news will bring them anxiety and pain, but could also strengthen your relationship. The alternative is that some

members of your family will shun you. If you're gay don't assume your family don't know if you haven't come out to them. They may have chosen to ignore 'that part of your life', perhaps inventing their own excuses. Not telling parents could eventually make them even more upset. You know your family better than anyone else, it might be a gamble, but it's your decision.

Your culture may make it impossible to discuss HIV with your family and friends. There are many organisations and helplines who may be able to put you in touch with other people in a similar situation to you who might be able to offer support or listen to your concerns.

Choosing to have children

Many women feel that because they or their partner are HIV positive, they can't have children. This is not the case although there are a number of issues that need to be considered.

If your partner is not HIV positive then it's likely neither of you wants him to become infected. But if you want to have children then unsafe sex is a risky option for him. To get around this many couples try artificial insemination, so that there is no risk of infection.

If both partners are HIV positive, sexual intercourse without a condom can still be risky. This is because there are different strains of the virus. If a person is re-infected with a different strain, then the new strain could take over.

When the man is HIV positive, some couples choose to use the technique known as 'sperm washing'. Sperm washing is when the semen of an HIV positive man is literally washed free of HIV. Far more research into this technique is necessary, as we don't yet know how effective it is. Sperm washing is only available on a limited basis in the UK.

Ensuring her unborn child is uninfected is usually a high priority for an infected pregnant woman. But at the same time it is important to get the balance right between taking drugs to reduce the risk of the child being infected and the mother taking the right drugs to remain in a good state of health. Treatment decisions have to be made reflecting both long- and short-term considerations to benefit both mother and child.

Some infected women believe that it is best to delay having children to see how treatments develop. However if pregnancy is delayed too long there is a risk that the woman will develop AIDS during the pregnancy which increases the risk of the unborn child being infected.

• The above information is an extract from AVERT's web site which can be found at www.avert.org Alternatively, see page 41 for their address details.

© AVERT

Living well with HIV

Frequently asked questions about sex and relationships when you're HIV positive

Is it still possible to have sex and relationships if I have HIV?
Not only is it still possible to continue to have sex and relationships when you're HIV positive, it is a very important part of life that people ought to be supported to continue.

The instinct to have sex and be close to someone is an integral part of being human. These needs do not go away because of HIV.

It is inappropriate to try to suppress sexual urges in order to avoid the spread of the virus, as often this can put people with HIV in a position where we are less, rather than more able, to make sure sex is safer, to protect our own health and that of others.

What are my responsibilities ?
There is no one clear definition, agreed by everyone, of the responsibilities of people with HIV when it comes to sex and relationships. Some would say the responsibility is to always tell people you have HIV, others to avoid sex altogether.

In reality, the responsibility is shared between both infected and uninfected people to strive toward avoiding transmission, whilst continuing to have as full and normal a life as possible.

We recognise that people do not always have clear or exaggerated ideas of their responsibilities, and that people will not always succeed in fulfilling them.

Far from being condemned for this, it is more effective to support people to understand and meet them in the future.

• The above information is from the Terrence Higgins Trust web site which can be found at ww.tht.org.uk

© Terrence Higgins Trust

THE MOST IMPORTANT THING ABOUT BEING HIV POSITIVE IS — — BEING POSITIVELY HUMAN!!

Deciding whether to have an HIV test

Information from the Terrence Higgins Trust

Have you been at risk?

If you have not been at risk of exposure to HIV, there is no reason for having an HIV test. If you are not sure about how HIV is passed on, or you would like more information or you would like to talk to someone about your situation, phone the Terrence Higgins Trust Helpline on 020 7242 1010. The Terrence Higgins Trust booklet *A guide to protecting yourself and others from HIV infection* gives information about HIV transmission.

You may decide to have an HIV test so you can know

If you are concerned that you might be HIV positive, you may feel you want to know and end the uncertainty. Many people have found that actually knowing, instead of guessing, has helped them feel more in control.

If you go for an HIV test, it is important to be prepared for a result different from the one you may have been expecting. If you feel that you have not been exposed to HIV and are expecting a negative result, be aware that the result could be positive. You may actually have been exposed to HIV.

Try to prepare yourself for either result. If you test HIV positive, the news can be a great shock, even if you were expecting it. You will be faced with the knowledge that you are living with an unpredictable virus. You may be in good health and could remain healthy for many years, but you could also become ill.

Sometimes, people decide to test because they want to prepare themselves mentally for the possibility that they might become ill. Even if you know you have been at risk, discovering you have HIV only when you develop an HIV-related condition and are perhaps very sick can be a double shock.

For some people the most important question may not be *whether* to have an HIV test but *when*. Is now the right time for you to learn whether you have HIV? You might be HIV positive – do you want to deal with this knowledge now, or would you prefer to wait until you feel ready?

Having an HIV test so you can look after your health

Combination therapy

Taking a combination of three or more anti-HIV drugs has made a huge difference to the lives of people living with HIV. It is the most effective anti-HIV treatment so far developed and many who were seriously ill before beginning therapy have returned to good health. For many who know they have been at risk, access to combination therapy is a powerful reason for having an HIV test. Such therapy can prevent you falling ill provided it is taken correctly.

However, it is important to remember that combination therapy is not perfect and is certainly not a cure for HIV.

If you go for an HIV test, it is important to be prepared for a result different from the one you may have been expecting

---

Doctors' views differ on the best time to start combination therapy. You will probably not be offered combination therapy immediately if you test positive, unless you are already ill. However, it is generally accepted that the best option is to limit, as much as possible, damage to your immune system. This damage is measured by regular blood tests to measure CD4 counts and viral load levels. Doctors will advise starting treatment as soon as your regular blood tests indicate that HIV has caused damage to the immune system. This will be the case even if you are well.

You can talk about your treatment options with the health care team at a testing clinic before you have a test or with one of the organisations which offer treatment support services. See also the Terrence Higgins Trust booklets *Living with HIV* and *A Guide to Starting Combination Therapy* for more information about drug treatments for HIV.

Preventing opportunistic infections

One of the main benefits of combination therapy for people who have no HIV-related symptoms is that it can prevent the HIV infection from progressing further. For people who have had HIV-related symptoms, combination therapy has usually resulted in symptoms improving or disappearing, and it has also reduced their future risk of developing further HIV-related symptoms.

After a few weeks of combination therapy, many people have reported increases in their levels of energy and general sense of well-being. However, many others do suffer from bad side effects.

If you are HIV positive, regular tests of your blood will show whether you are becoming vulnerable. For some people who know they have been at risk, this is another reason to have an HIV test.

Healthy living

Some people want to know whether they have HIV so that they can take extra care of their health if they are HIV positive. A healthy, balanced diet and regular exercise will help safeguard your health if you have HIV. On the other hand, stress, smoking, heavy drinking and recreational drug use all put a strain on your immune system. Food hygiene is particularly important if your immune system is damaged, as bacteria could make you very ill. Many people with HIV use complementary therapies, such as massage, acupuncture and herbal treatments, to help control symptoms or stress and increase their sense of well-being.

If you are ill

If you are ill and your doctor thinks your illness may be HIV-related, an HIV test will help the doctor decide how to treat you. However, it is still your choice whether you have a test. If you are ill and an HIV test shows you to be HIV positive, your doctor will suggest that you start combination therapy immediately.

• The above information is an extract from *Is it time to test? – A guide to HIV testing issues*, produced by the Terrence Higgins Trust. See page 41 for address details.

© *Terrence Higgins Trust*

Preventing HIV/AIDS among young people

Information from the United Nations Department of Public Information and UNAIDS

Young people are at the centre of the HIV/AIDS epidemic. Their behaviour, the extent to which their rights are protected, and the services and information they receive determine the quality of life of millions of people. Young people are particularly susceptible to HIV infection and they also carry the burden of caring for family members living with HIV/AIDS. Around the world, AIDS is shattering young people's opportunities for healthy adult lives. Nevertheless, it is young people who offer the greatest hope for changing the course of the epidemic.

At the hub of the epidemic

• An estimated 10.3 million people aged 15-24 are living with HIV/AIDS, and half of all new infections – over 7,000 daily – are occurring among young people.
• Sub-Saharan Africa is hardest hit. It is home to over 70% of young people living with HIV/AIDS and to 90% of the AIDS orphans in the world (12.1 million children).
• Young people are vulnerable to HIV because of risky sexual behaviour, substance use and their lack of access to HIV information and prevention services.

• Ignorance about the epidemic remains pervasive among young people, many of whom do not know how to protect themselves from HIV. In Mozambique, for example, 74% of girls and 62% of boys aged 15-19 are unaware of any way to protect themselves. Half of the teenage girls in sub-Saharan Africa do not realise that a healthy-looking person can be living with HIV/AIDS.
• Marginalised young people (including street children, refugees and migrants) may be at particular risk because of stigma, their exposure to unprotected sex (in exchange for food, protection or money) and the use of illicit drugs.

Young people and sexual behaviour

• Many young people do not believe that HIV is a threat to them. Almost two-thirds of

---

Ignorance about the epidemic remains pervasive among young people, many of whom do not know how to protect themselves from HIV

---

sexually active girls aged 15-19 in Haiti do not believe they run the risk of HIV infection; more than half of their Zimbabwean counterparts share that perception.
• Some adolescents become sexually active early, without the benefit of the necessary information, skills and services to protect themselves from HIV. Programmes targeting young people often fail to acknowledge such early sexual activity.
• Sexual relations are often unplanned and sometimes coerced. Of the estimated 2 million sex workers in India, 20% are under the age of 15 and nearly 50% are under 18. Forced sex can injure the genital tract, thereby increasing the odds of acquiring HIV and other sexually transmitted infections.
• Young people exposed to sexual abuse and exploitation (including incest, rape and forced prostitution) are especially vulnerable to HIV infection. In Cambodia, 30% of sex workers aged 13-19 are infected with HIV.
• Stigma, social exclusion and a lack of information put young men who have sex with men at additional risk. Among self-

identified homosexual young men in Peru, 40% have reported recent unprotected anal intercourse.

- Good-quality sexual health education programmes help delay the onset of sexual activity and protect sexually active young people from HIV, other sexually transmitted infections and pregnancy.

- Many factors discourage young people from using health services. They include a lack of privacy and confidentiality, insensitive staff, threatening environments, an inability to afford services, and the fact that services often do not cater to unaccompanied minors or are restricted to married adults.

- Biological, social and economic factors make young women especially vulnerable to HIV, occasionally leading to infection soon after the women have become sexually active. A study in Zambia found that, within a year of becoming sexually active, 18% of young women surveyed were HIV-positive.

- In some of the worst-affected countries, adolescent girls are being infected at a rate five-to-six times higher than are boys. There is growing evidence that older men are responsible for a large share of these infections.

Young people and substance use

- Drug infection features prominently in the epidemic, notably in the many countries where injecting drug users are forced to live on the margins of society and lack access to HIV/AIDS information and prevention programmes. Many of these users are young.

- The use of alcohol and other drugs is associated with unsafe sexual behaviour. HIV prevention strategies need to address this issue.

Respecting and involving young people

- Young people are key to controlling HIV/AIDS. They have the right to knowledge and skills that reduce their vulnerability and enable them to protect themselves and each other against the epidemic. Experiences show that HIV/AIDS programmes that respect and involve young people, while being sensitive to their cultures, are more likely to succeed.

- Bigger and better communication and social mobilisation efforts are needed to broaden HIV/AIDS awareness and promote healthy lifestyles. They also need to defuse the stigma and discrimination associated with HIV/AIDS.

- Young people need a safe and supportive environment. This requires sensitive attitudes, policies and legislation at family, community and national levels. Sturdy relationships with caring parents or other adult role models are essential.

- Strong and effective education systems are important. Yet, in many countries, those systems are in disarray. They need to be repaired and boosted with innovative teaching approaches.

- Outreach and peer education programmes among young drug users should be expanded. They can include steps to improve access to information, prevention commodities (such as condoms and sterile injecting equipment for those who inject), as well as HIV/AIDS prevention and care services.

Targets for success

- Governments have pledged to cut HIV prevalence among 15- to 24-year-olds by a quarter in the most affected countries by 2005, and globally by 2010.

- They have also undertaken to ensure that, by 2005, at least 90% of young people have access to information, education and services to reduce their vulnerability to HIV infection. Such services should include access to preventive methods such as female and male condoms, voluntary testing, counselling and follow-up support.

• The above information is an extract from the publication *Global Crisis – Global Action*, published by the United Nations Department of Public Information and UNAIDS.

© United Nations Department of Public Information and UNAIDS

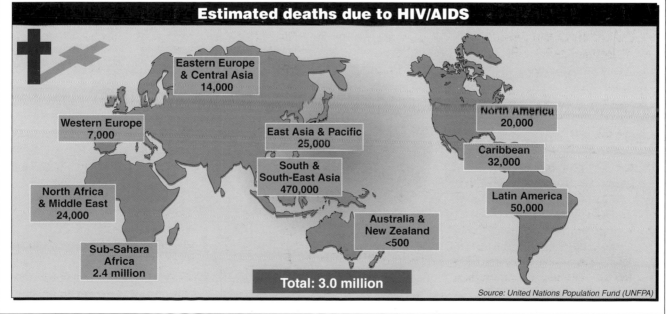

Estimated deaths due to HIV/AIDS

- Eastern Europe & Central Asia 14,000
- Western Europe 7,000
- East Asia & Pacific 25,000
- South & South-East Asia 470,000
- North Africa & Middle East 24,000
- Sub-Sahara Africa 2.4 million
- Australia & New Zealand <500
- North America 20,000
- Caribbean 32,000
- Latin America 50,000

Total: 3.0 million

Source: United Nations Population Fund (UNFPA)

HIV/AIDS – the threat to Asia

Information from Save the Children

The rapid spread of HIV/AIDS across Asia and the Pacific represents a serious threat to enormous numbers of people should the epidemic reach the devastating levels seen in sub-Saharan Africa. 5.8 million adults and children were already living with HIV/AIDS in South and South-East Asia at the end of 2000, while 850,000 children under 15 had lost one or both parents by the end of 1999 and the numbers are increasing rapidly. In particular, the impact on children and young people affects every aspect of their lives, from loss of parents and access to education and health services, apart from the risk of the disease itself.

Conflict, with the resulting instability and cross-border movements of large numbers of people, the high density of population, extreme levels of poverty and the cultural backgrounds in the area combine to create conditions in which the epidemic will spread rapidly unless action is taken urgently on a number of fronts.

Doug Webb, HIV/AIDS Adviser at Save the Children UK, says: 'Millions of children whose lives were already difficult have been further devastated by the direct and indirect effects of HIV/AIDS, not only in Asia and the Pacific, but all round the world. It's not enough to pick up on just one or two of the most visible causes such as drugs provision if the long-term fight against HIV/AIDS is to be won. The international community must accept responsibility for ensuring that the work continues on all fronts – and that practical, sustained and sustainable solutions are found.'

Other important factors in the spread of HIV/AIDS can and are being overcome with current work in the field. As one of the leading organisations helping communities

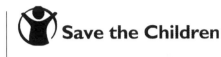
Save the Children

throughout the world improve the quality of care and support for those already infected and affected by HIV/AIDS, Save the Children is presenting six major papers on its project work in Asia at the Sixth International Conference on AIDS in Asia and the Pacific (ICAAP) from 5 to 10 October 2001 in Melbourne. These projects demonstrate what can be achieved through working with the local communities to contain the spread of the disease and reduce its impact on those communities and the children and young people in them.

They also highlight a number of key issues that apply across the region, including:

- Community-based approaches are effective in changing behaviour.
- Strategic partnerships greatly enhance the impact and sustainability of HIV/AIDS programmes, enabling them to operate effectively across borders.
- Culturally and politically sensitive approaches are essential in developing programmes for children and young people, especially in cultures where talking to them about sex, sexuality and sexual and reproductive health is considered taboo.
- Integrating sexual health education activities into existing community activities increases their impact.
- Involving young people at all stages of project development is essential to ensure their needs are being met and to provide a sense of ownership of the projects.

A document, *Young People and HIV/AIDS – responding to the new Asian crisis*, containing case studies and abstracts from the ICAAP presentations, is available from Save the Children.

• The above information is from Save the Children's web site: www.savethechildren.org.uk

© *Save the Children*

China in the grip of 'hidden Aids epidemic'

By David Rennie in Beijing

A senior health official yesterday painted a bleak picture of Aids in China as an accelerating epidemic caused by intravenous drug use, rampant prostitution and a tainted blood industry.

Yin Dakui, the deputy health minister, estimated there were 600,000 Chinese with HIV or Aids. Experts working in China said this was a serious underestimate.

Few incentives are offered for people to be tested and most citizens do not get free healthcare. An HIV diagnosis is seen as a death sentence, prompting ostracism and probably the loss of their job.

High-risk groups, such as drug users and prostitutes, live in fear of prosecution. Homosexuality is barely acknowledged. 'People prefer to live in ignorance,' said a Western aid official.

The central government is hamstrung by local officials who suppress all news of the disease and aggressively thwart testing by outsiders, fearing the stigma of becoming an 'Aids area'.

By June, China had 26,000 reported cases of HIV-Aids. The rate of increase year on year was 67 per cent, but Mr Yin said China hoped to cut it to nearly zero by the end of the decade.

China had no funds for expensive 'drug cocktails', he said. A limited supply of unproven traditional Chinese medicines is used instead to ease symptoms.

Mr Yin offered the first official admission that tens of thousands of peasants got HIV after selling blood products such as plasma to illegal blood stations in the Nineties.

His words vindicated the band of Chinese doctors and journalists who battled censorship and harassment to give news of the Aids tragedy to the outside world.

Mr Yin said 50,000 people were believed to have contracted HIV by selling their blood to illegal traders.

A much smaller number had contracted HIV from blood transfusions, he added.

One Aids specialist dismissed the figures as a gross understatement. He spoke of infection rates of up to 70 per cent among peasants who sold

> **By June, China had 26,000 reported cases of HIV-Aids. The rate of increase year on year was 67 per cent**

blood in the central province of Henan.

The senior physician, who asked for anonymity to avoid 'political problems', said the true dangers of receiving blood transfusions in China were still unknown. 'A lot of people who received blood have not fallen sick yet.'

Mr Yin's figures seemed to show that blood transfusion patients ran high risks of infection. In the worst-hit areas, one in every 2,500 transfusions transmitted HIV, he said.

China hoped to cut the rate to one in 100,000 nationally, and to one in 10,000 in infection blackspots, within four years.

South Africa shaken by Aids survey

By Christopher Munnion in Johannesburg

Aids will have claimed the lives of more than six million South Africans – a fifth of the population – by 2010, the country's medical research council reported yesterday.

The results of a survey based on official statistics contradicted President Thabo Mbeki's denial last week that Aids was the single largest killer in South Africa.

Estimates that 40 per cent of deaths in the country in the 15 to 49 age group were from Aids will revive the anger among campaigners over the South African leader's controversial views on the virus.

The report found an alarming increase in Aids-related deaths among young adults in the past three years. Unless there was effective intervention there would be a threefold increase in deaths among children between one and five.

Mr Mbeki shocked delegates to a world anti-Aids conference in Durban last year by asserting that there was no positive link between the HIV virus and the Aids pandemic.

He seemed to align himself to the highly-contentious views of the Aids dissidents in America and insisted, despite overwhelming medical opinion, that the HIV virus was caused by poverty.

Mr Mbeki restated his views last week by claiming that Aids caused only 2.2 per cent of deaths in South Africa, statistics he apparently gleaned from the internet on a now-outdated 1995 World Health Organisation report.

The WHO later pointed out that when people die of Aids-related illnesses, Aids is rarely given as the cause.

Expanding on experience

Prevention. This is a central objective of UNFPA in the global fight against HIV/AIDS. Among the many complex issues compounding the pandemic, prevention is the challenge that fits the agency best. For more than 30 years, UNFPA has supported a highly focused agenda to improve reproductive and sexual health.

The need for prevention is in the numbers:

- 5.3 million people were newly infected with HIV in 2000;
- Over half of new infections are among young people;
- More than 70 per cent of HIV infections worldwide occur via heterosexual sex;
- Young women are more vulnerable than young men – in some African countries, average rates in teenage girls are over five times higher than those in teenage boys;
- 95 per cent of all people infected with HIV live in developing countries. Africa is home to 70 per cent of the adults and 80 per cent of the children living with HIV/AIDS in the world.[1]

Thoraya A. Obaid, UNFPA Executive Director, defines the Fund's role: 'UNFPA is dedicating the very best it has to offer to the fight against HIV/AIDS. Our partners in UNAIDS, in governments, and in local schools and clinics each have their own strengths. Thirty years of experience in sexual and reproductive matters gives us our comparative advantage, a term that means: Here is what we can do best. The Fund will focus in particular on preventing HIV infection among young people and pregnant women through comprehensive programmes for prevention. Short-term interventions include abstinence, delaying the age of sexual activity, counselling to promote safe and healthy sexual behaviours, and condom use. Longer-term actions support lasting behaviour change. We will continue to be extensively

involved in providing overall leadership and advocacy to assist other organisations.'

Strategic directions

Preventing sexually transmitted diseases (STDs) has been a significant component of all reproductive health programmes supported by UNFPA since its founding in 1969. In the early 1990s, the Fund joined forces with UN agencies, governments and NGOs to fight the escalating HIV/AIDS pandemic. In 2000, UNFPA prepared to accelerate its activities at all levels and started to develop a guide for future action: UNFPA Strategic Directions for the Prevention of HIV Infection.

The new strategy expands on experience, defining a niche for UNFPA in three areas:

1. Preventing the sexual transmission of HIV, particularly through interventions that promote safe sexual behaviour among young people, including abstinence and delaying the age of sexual activity;
2. Condom programming to improve access to and use of condoms (male and female), taking into account user needs and perspectives;
3. Preventing HIV infection among pregnant women and its transmission to children and to HIV-negative partners.

It establishes for the first time a set of tools and guidelines for use in programme design and implementation within the Fund.

Ways UNFPA is working to prevent HIV/AIDS

While other partners bring their comparative advantages to the care and treatment of people living with HIV/AIDS, to children and to injecting drug users, for example, UNFPA is uniquely positioned to advance prevention. Elements of the UNFPA comparative advantage include:

- Existence of a strong network of partners and a strong country presence;
- HIV/AIDS advisers in regional, multi-disciplinary Country Technical Services Teams (CSTs);
- Expertise in negotiating with governments to guarantee access to reproductive health, including

family planning and sexual health information, services and commodities;

- More than 30 years of programme experience addressing sensitive issues such as gender relations and sexuality in various sociocultural settings.

The strategy supports UNFPA's main objective: to help ensure universal access to high-quality reproductive health services to all couples and individuals by 2015. It also reflects the Programme of Action of the 1994 International Conference on Population and Development (ICPD) and the goals set at its five-year review (ICPD+5). The ICPD guides UNFPA and places responsibility on the Fund to provide leadership in matters of sexual and reproductive health. The Fund also contributes to the operationalisation of the UNAIDS Framework for Global Leadership on HIV/AIDS.[2]

References
1 UNAIDS, AIDS Epidemic Update: December 2000.

2 The UNAIDS Framework for Global Leadership on HIV/AIDS, December 2000, guides the development of the United Nations system strategic plan. The Framework endorses an 'expanded response' to the pandemic, defined as one that simultaneously reduces risk, vulnerability and impact.

- The above information is from the UNFPA's web site which can be found at www.unfpa.org

Moving forward together

Information from the International Planned Parenthood Federation (IPPF)

A crisis in the availability of reproductive health supplies, in particular contraceptives and condoms for HIV/AIDS prevention, is threatening human rights and the realisation of the goals of the 1994 International Conference on Population and Development, delegates at 'Meeting the Reproductive Health Challenge: Securing Contraceptives and Condoms for HIV/AIDS Prevention' conference in Istanbul heard (3-5 May 2001).

It is estimated that 105 billion condoms are needed worldwide over the next 15 years yet funding for reproductive health, including the supply of condoms, decreased by 26% in the year 2000 alone, the conference heard.

Half of all pregnancies are unintended. Every minute, 40 women undergo an unsafe abortion; ten people are infected with HIV/AIDS and 650 people are infected with a curable sexually transmitted infection (STI). This reality is compounded by the largest ever generation of young people aged 15-24, the rapidly growing demand for family planning and other reproductive health services as well as the global AIDS pandemic.

The world shortage of condoms was one of the main issues discussed at the meeting of nearly 70 non-governmental organisations, governments, private foundations, bilateral and multilateral agencies. Key players, including IPPF, gathered to develop concrete and immediate actions to meet the challenge of securing reproductive health supplies.

The crisis has been compounded by President Bush's moves to shut off federal aid to overseas family planning centres should abortion be so much as mentioned. The ending of US federal aid to family planning centres overseas means there is also less money for condoms, now the most important means of preventing the spread of HIV/AIDS.

'It is a crime that in this modern age we don't have the infrastructure to ensure condoms reach the countries most affected by HIV/AIDS,' said Ingar Brueggemann, Director-General of

---

Half of all pregnancies are unintended. Every minute, 40 women undergo an unsafe abortion; ten people are infected with HIV/AIDS and 650 people are infected with a curable sexually transmitted infection

---

the International Planned Parenthood Federation (IPPF). 'Again, it will be poor countries that suffer unless we act now to ensure supplies get through.'

In recognition of this global crisis participants at the meeting agreed that:

- There is an urgent need to build awareness of and generate action on this crisis.
- Response strategies must be country-specific, designed and led by governments that fully involve civil society, and flexibly supported by donors.
- Prevention of unintended pregnancies and STIs, especially HIV/AIDS, is a cornerstone of good reproductive health care and must have priority within sector strategies and budgets.
- Effective implementation demands clearly defined roles, responsibilities and accountability for all partners.
- UNFPA's mandate to assist countries in ensuring availability of and access to reproductive health supplies and services is a critical component of this effort.

- The above information is from the International Planned Parenthood Federation's (IPPF) web site which can be found at www.ippf.org

AIDS education

A battle against ignorance

Many of the 36.1 million people infected with HIV do not know they are carrying the virus. Nor do they know much about the disease. Education could have helped them avoid acquiring the virus. Education is a vital step towards halting the epidemic and overcoming the prejudice and fear faced by people living with HIV/AIDS.

- Preventive education programmes should reach everyone – especially young people, among whom about half of all new HIV infections are occurring. The best educational programmes seek to empower women by providing them with information, skills and services that help them protect themselves.
- If HIV/AIDS preventive education is to be effective, it must occur through all avenues of education (formal and non-formal), through schools and through broader community channels with strong political support. It should also match the various linguistic, social and cultural realities of the groups being addressed.
- Uganda has cut its HIV prevalence rates significantly – from an estimated 14% in the early 1990s to around 8% in 2000 – thanks to extensive preventive education campaigns that mobilised leaders at all levels and in all sectors.
- Widespread education efforts, including those mounted by a network of self-help organisations, have enabled Senegal to maintain its HIV prevalence rates below 2%. Massive education campaigns have also helped Brazil and Thailand make strong strides towards managing their epidemics.

Tailoring the message

- Since people have different frames of reference, preventive information cannot be of a one-

size-fits-all variety. It has to be customised for different audiences. Surveys and assessment studies that reveal the local dynamics of the epidemic and that identify local attitudes and needs make it possible to tailor prevention messages effectively.
- A condom campaign launched in Ghana in 2000 showed how effectively messages could be adapted to local circumstances. Using street theatre and rap performers, the campaign triggered an 80% rise in condom use in just six months. In South Africa, popular television formats are being successfully used to raise awareness of HIV/AIDS.
- Information campaigns and skill-building are important elements of preventive education. The scope of the epidemic means that such campaigns should involve the public and private sectors, as well as non-governmental organisations, on a scale unparalleled in the history of communication.
- In some parts of the world, AIDS is also striking countries' education systems. In some countries, up to 30% of teachers are directly affected by the epidemic. Pre-

ventive education therefore has to include teachers and others working in education, as well as their families.
- Preventive education must take into account – and help change – ingrained cultural habits that leave sections of society (particularly women) more vulnerable to infection and less able to cope with the effects of the disease. Misguided notions of masculinity, for example, often deprive women and girls of control over their bodies.
- All educational programmes must reach girls and women to equip them with the information and skills that can help them protect themselves against HIV/AIDS.
- It is crucial that the protection of human rights serves as the basis for education campaigns to stop the exclusion of people living with HIV/AIDS and give them access to care.

• The above information is an extract from the publication *Global Crisis – Global Action*, published by the United Nations Department of Public Information and UNAIDS.

© United Nations Department of Public Information and UNAIDS

The search for an HIV vaccine

Information from the United Nations Department of Public Information and UNAIDS

Soon after the identification of the human immunodeficiency virus (HIV) in 1983, some health officials were predicting that a vaccine would be developed within a couple of years. The search has proven to be much more difficult than anticipated, but scientists are confident that an HIV vaccine will be discovered.

- The quest for an HIV vaccine dates back to 1987, when the first human trial of a candidate HIV vaccine was conducted in the United States. About 30 experimental vaccines have since been tested in some 60 trials.

- So far, most of the trials have been staged in industrialised countries, but now trials are increasingly being done in developing countries also. During the 1990s, several vaccine initiatives were launched in developing countries, including Africa.

- A vaccine will not be a panacea, nor will it be an alternative to prevention. Because an eventual vaccine is unlikely to be 100% effective, it will have to be used alongside wide-ranging and effective prevention programmes. In fact, once a vaccine is developed, awareness-raising and prevention efforts will need to be redoubled in order to counter the risk of complacency.

- An HIV vaccine must benefit all humanity. Once discovered, the vaccine will have to be made available to everyone with minimum delay, in sufficient quantities and at affordable prices. Early planning is needed to ensure that this is achieved.

A massive challenge

- The peculiarities of the virus make the development of an HIV vaccine an arduous and expensive process. Still lacking, for instance, is the clear scientific understanding required to guide the pharmaceutical development of specific candidate vaccines.

- HIV/AIDS differs profoundly from most other infectious diseases. In the case of the latter, the body develops an immune response to an infection in order to protect itself and help it recover from disease. A successful vaccine against such diseases therefore stimulates effective immune responses. But HIV immobilises the body's immune responses, leaving them incapable of controlling infection or preventing disease.

- Most existing vaccines are based on an entire microorganism (virus or bacterium) that has been killed or rendered harmless. In the case of HIV, however, those 'classical' vaccine approaches are not considered sufficiently safe. Experimental HIV vaccines therefore are based on *parts* of the virus (to ensure that vaccination does not result in HIV infection). This makes the development of a vaccine even more challenging.

- Ten subtypes of the HIV virus have already been identified. Scientists do not yet know whether a vaccine will have to be prepared for each subtype or whether a more broadly protective vaccine will be possible. That, coupled with the fact that the subtypes in developing countries differ from those prevalent in the industrialised world, makes it essential that experimental vaccines be developed simultaneously in the North and South.

- Scientists know that the development of a vaccine is possible (because animals can be protected against HIV infection), but they remain uncertain as to whether that success can be extrapolated to humans. For that reason, the search for an HIV vaccine has to include human trials, which are costly and time-consuming

A long process

- The quest for an HIV vaccine takes many years. Experimental vaccines are first tested on animals, and the best vaccine candidates can then be selected for possible testing on humans. Testing is then carried out on HIV-negative volunteers, in three phases. Only in the last phase does it become clear whether the vaccine works.
- Phase I tests are done on 20-40 volunteers. These tests are intended to confirm the vaccine's safety and determine whether it triggers strong enough levels of HIV-specific immune responses.
- Phase II tests involve hundreds of volunteers and are intended to further check vaccine safety and assess the potency of immune responses.
- Phase III tests involve large-scale field trials, involving thousands of volunteers. The aim is to gauge whether the candidate vaccine indeed protects against HIV infection or the onset of AIDS. The trials last for up to four years.
- About 30 experimental HIV vaccines have been tested since 1987 – all of them in Phase I or II trials – and the bulk of them in the United States and Western Europe. Since 1993, however, 13 such trials have been conducted

> *Once a vaccine is developed, awareness-raising and prevention efforts will need to be redoubled in order to counter the risk of complacency*

in the South – in Brazil, China, Cuba, Haiti, Kenya, Thailand and Uganda. In some of these trials, scientists have determined that experimental vaccines are safe and that some stimulate anti-HIV responses in the body. But they do not yet know whether the vaccines would protect people against infection. That can only be determined in Phase III trials, which are ethically, logistically and scientifically complicated.
- By mid-2001, two efficacy (Phase III) trials were under way. One, in the United States, was based on subtype B of the virus, while the other, in Thailand, was based on subtype BE. Initial results are expected towards the end of 2001.
- Numerous other vaccine endeavours are under way. In the African AIDS Vaccine Programme, announced in Nairobi in June 2000, African scientists, governments and institutions are

teaming up to develop a vaccine that can help turn the epidemic around on that continent. They aim to complete at least one efficacy trial by 2007. Also active in the quest is the International AIDS Vaccine Initiative, a research consortium started in 1996 and supported by government and private grants. It is committed to ensuring that rich and poor countries alike get simultaneous access to a vaccine.

Everybody's duty

- The duty of developing a vaccine rests with the entire international community. But the wealthy countries (and the pharmaceutical industry) have the human, financial and technical resources to speed up the research and development of vaccines that are appropriate for use in developing countries. At the same time, developing countries have a key role to play, not least in conducting relevant clinical trials to prove vaccine efficacy.

• The above information is an extract from the publication *Global Crisis – Global Action*, published by the United Nations Department of Public Information and UNAIDS.

© United Nations Department of Public Information and UNAIDS

Estimated number of adults and children living with HIV/AIDS, end 1999

South Africa	4,700,000
India	3,700,000
Ethiopia	3,000,000
Nigeria	2,700,000
Kenya	2,100,000
Zimbabwe	1,500,000
United Republic of Tanzania	1,300,000
Mozambique	1,200,000
Democratic Republic of Congo	1,100,000
Zambia	870,000
USA	870,000
Uganda	850,000
Malawi	820,000
Côte d'Ivoire	800,000
Thailand	695,000

* End 2000 estimates; National AIDS Programme

Source: Joint United Nations Programme on HIV/AIDS (UNAIDS) 2001

ADDITIONAL RESOURCES

You might like to contact the following organisations for further information. Due to the increasing cost of postage, many organisations cannot respond to enquiries unless they receive a stamped, addressed envelope.

AVERT
4 Brighton Road
Horsham
West Sussex
RH13 5BA
Tel: 01403 210202
Fax: 01403 211001
E-mail: avert@dial.pipex.com
Web site: www.avert.org
AVERT is a leading UK AIDS
Education and Medical Research
charity. They are responsible for a
wide range of education and
medical research work. Publish a
wide range of educational material
on the issues of homosexuality.
Ask for their Resources Catalogue.

**fpa (formerly The Family
Planning Association)**
2-12 Pentonville Road
London
N1 9FP
Tel: 020 7837 5432
Fax: 020 7837 3042
Web site: www.fpa.org.uk
Produces information and
publications on all aspects of
reproduction and sexual health –
phone for a publications catalogue.
The Helpline on 020 7837 4044
Monday-Friday 9am to 7pm is run
by qualified healthcare workers
and can answer queries on all
aspects of family planning.

**International Planned Parenthood
Federation (IPPF)**
Regent's College
Inner Circle
Regent's Park
London
NW1 4NS
Tel: 020 7487 7900
Fax: 020 7487 7950
E-mail: info@ippf.org
Web site: www.ippf.org
The largest voluntary organisation
in the field of sexual and
reproductive health including
family planning, represented in
over 180 countries worldwide.

Public Health Laboratory Service
61 Collingdale Avenue
Collingdale
London
NW9 5DF
Tel: 020 8200 1295
Fax: 020 8200 8130
Web site: www.phls.co.uk
The Public Health Laboratory
Service (PHLS) protects the
population from infection by
detecting, diagnosing, and
monitoring communicable
diseases. It provides evidence for
action to prevent and control
infectious disease threats to
individuals and populations.

Save the Children
17 Grove Lane
Camberwell
London
SE5 8RD
Tel: 020 7703 5400
Fax: 020 7703 2278
Web site:
www.savethechildren.org.uk
Save the Children is the leading
UK charity working to create a
better world for children. We work
in 70 countries helping children in
the world's most impoverished
communities. We are part of the
International Save the Children
Alliance, which aims to be a truly
international movement for
children. Produce a wide range of
materials. Ask for their catalogue.

Terrence Higgins Trust
52-54 Gray's Inn Road
London, WC1X 8JU
Tel: 020 7831 0330
Fax: 020 7242 0121
E-mail: info@tht.org.uk
Web site: www.tht.org.uk
Works to promote an
understanding of HIV and AIDS
issues by collecting and
disseminating medical and social
information. Runs a phone
helpline. Provides training and
practical support for people with
AIDS and their family and friends.

UNAIDS
20, Avenue Appia
CH-1211 Geneva
Switzerland
Tel; + 41 22 791 3666
Fax: + 41 22 791 4187
E-mail: unaids@unaids.org
Web site: www.unaids.org
As the leading advocate for
worldwide action against HIV/
AIDS, the global mission of
UNAIDS is to lead, strengthen
and support an expanded response
to the epidemic that will prevent
the spread of HIV, provide care
and support for those infected and
affected by the disease, reduce the
vulnerability of individuals and
communities to HIV/AIDS,
alleviate the socio-economic and
human impact of the epidemic.

**United Nations Population Fund
(UNFPA)**
220 East 42nd Street
New York NY10017
USA
Tel: + 1 212 297 5279
Fax: + 1 212 557 6416
E-mail: hq@unfpa.org
Web site: www.unfpa.org
UNFPA, the United Nations
Population Fund, helps developing
countries find solutions to their
population problems. Publishes
The State of World Population, an
annual report highlighting new
developments in population. Also
publishes many other titles and
information on various aspects of
the issue of population.

INDEX

ACKNOWLEDGEMENTS

The publisher is grateful for permission to reproduce the following material.

While every care has been taken to trace and acknowledge copyright, the publisher tenders its apology for any accidental infringement or where copyright has proved untraceable. The publisher would be pleased to come to a suitable arrangement in any such case with the rightful owner.

Chapter One: Sexual Health

Sexual health in England today – setting the scene, © Crown copyright is reproduced with the permission of the Controller of Her Majesty's Stationery Office, *Newly reported HIV infections*, © Crown copyright is reproduced with the permission of the Controller of Her Majesty's Stationery Office, *Government to spend £4m on safe sex campaign*, © Guardian Newspapers Limited 2001, *Sexually transmitted infections*, © fpa, *Sexually transmitted infections*, © Public Health Laboratory Service (PHLS), *Selected conditions by sex*, © Public Health Laboratory Service (PHLS), *Types of infections*, © fpa, *Sexual health for women*, © Health Promotion England, Crown copyright is reproduced with the permission of the Controller of Her Majesty's Stationery Office, *Sexual health for men*, © Health Promotion England, Crown copyright is reproduced with the permission of the Controller of Her Majesty's Stationery Office, *Fertility bug shock*, © The Daily Mail, September 2001, *Where to go for help*, © Health Promotion England, Crown copyright is reproduced with the permission of the Controller of Her Majesty's Stationery Office.

Chapter Two: HIV and AIDS

Aids – a global crisis, © Guardian Newspapers Limited 2001, *Facts about HIV/AIDS*, © United Nations Population Fund (UNFPA), *New infections of HIV*, © United Nations Population Fund (UNFPA), *Worldwide HIV & AIDS epidemic statistics*, © AVERT, *End-2000 global estimates, children and adults*, © United Nations Population Fund (UNFPA), *HIV and AIDS*, © AVERT, *40 per cent rise in Aids feared over next three years*, © Telegraph Group Limited, London 2001, *General information: HIV*, © Public Health Laboratory Service (PHLS), *Young men and HIV*, © United Nations Programme on HIV/AIDS (UNAIDS) and The Panos Institute 2001, *Estimated number of adults and children newly infected with HIV during 2000*, © United Nations Population Fund (UNFPA), *What happens when someone has HIV?*, © Terrence Higgins Trust, *Adults and children estimated to be living with HIV/AIDS as of end 2000*, © United Nations Population Fund (UNFPA), *Living with HIV*, © AVERT, *Living well with HIV*, © Terrence Higgins Trust, *Deciding whether to have an HIV test*, © Terrence Higgins Trust, *Preventing HIV/AIDS among young people*, © United Nations Department of Public Information and UNAIDS, *Estimated deaths due to HIV/AIDS*, © United Nations Population Fund (UNFPA), *HIV/AIDS – the threat to Asia*, © Save the Children, *China in the grip of 'hidden Aids epidemic'*, © Telegraph Group Limited, London 2001, *South Africa shaken by Aids survey*, © Telegraph Group Limited, London 2001, *Expanding on experience*, © United Nations Population Fund (UNFPA), *Moving forward together*, © International Planned Parenthood Federation (IPPF), *AIDS education*, © United Nations Department of Public Information and UNAIDS, *The search for an HIV vaccine*, © United Nations Department of Public Information and UNAIDS, *Estimated number of adults and children living with HIV/AIDS, end 1999*, © Joint United Nations Programme on HIV/AIDS (UNAIDS) 2001.

Photographs and illustrations:

Pages 8, 12, 14, 16, 28, 30, 36, 38: Simon Kneebone, pages 9, 13, 18, 27, 34, 39: Pumpkin House.

Craig Donnellan
Cambridge
January, 2002